WORKBOOK

FUTURE INTRO

English for Work, Life, and Academic Success

Second Edition

Series Consultants
Sarah Lynn
Ronna Magy
Federico Salas-Isnardi

Authors
Jennifer Asp
Kate Mueller

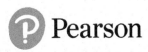

Future Intro Workbook
English for Work, Life, and Academic Success
Copyright © 2019 by Pearson Education, Inc.
All rights reserved. No part of this publication may be reproduced, stored in a retrieval system, or transmitted in any form or by any means, electronic, mechanical, photocopying, recording, or otherwise, without the prior permission of the publisher.

Pearson Education, 221 River Street, Hoboken, NJ 07030 USA

Staff credits: The people who made up the ***Future Intro Workbook*** team, representing content development, design, manufacturing, marketing, multimedia, project management, publishing, rights management, and testing, are Pietro Alongi, Jennifer Castro, Dave Dickey, Gina DiLillo, Warren Fischbach, Pamela Fishman, Gosia Jaros-White, Joanna Konieczna, Michael Mone, Mary Perrotta Rich, Katarzyna Starzyńska-Kościuszko, Claire Van Poperin, Joseph Vella, Gabby Wu.

Text composition: Dataflow International
Cover design: EMC Design Ltd
Audio: CityVox

ISBN-13: 978-0-13-454758-9
ISBN-10: 0-13-454758-6

Printed in the United States of America

12 2022

CONTENTS

The *Future Intro Workbook* has 12-page units to complement what students have learned in the Student Book. Each Workbook unit follows the lesson order of the Student Book and provides supplemental practice in vocabulary, listening and speaking, grammar, reading, writing, soft skills, and life skills. Students can complete the exercises outside the classroom as homework or during class to extend instruction.

The Workbook audio provides practice with conversations, grammar, and life skills competencies. In addition, the audio includes the readings from the Workbook so students can become more fluent readers.

UNIT STRUCTURE

Vocabulary

Each Workbook unit begins with vocabulary practice. There are usually three vocabulary lessons per unit that provide reinforcement activities for the vocabulary lessons in the Student Book. In addition, some of the Life Skills lessons contain relevant vocabulary practice.

Grammar

Grammar is practiced in contextualized exercises that include sentence completion, sentence writing, fill-in, matching, and multiple choice. Grammar exercises also reinforce the new vocabulary taught in that lesson. Some lessons include personalized activities.

Listening

Listening activities in the Workbook are used to complement various skills, including vocabulary, grammar, conversation, life skills, and reading. Activities include listening comprehension, listening dictation, listening and reading, and listening to check answers.

Life Skills

In the second edition, the Life Skills lesson has been revised to focus more on the real-life language and civic-literacy skills required today.

Realia-based exercises are usually featured on these pages. Students complete forms and other realia based on information provided or with their own information. Other activity types include fill-in, matching, and multiple choice.

Writing

Writing is practiced in controlled and personalized activities throughout the Workbook. In each lesson, students write words, phrases, and/or sentences.

Reading

The reading page extends the practice provided in the reading lesson in the Student Book. The story featured in the Student Book is presented again, but with the sentences scrambled. Students listen to the audio and number the sentences in the correct order. Then students write the story in the correct order.

English at Work

In the second edition, *Future* has further enhanced its development of workplace skills by adding an English at Work lesson to each unit. Soft skills are the critical interpersonal communication skills needed to succeed in any workplace. This page in the Workbook builds upon the English at Work lesson in the Student Book. It presents the conversation again, but with the lines scrambled. Students work to number the sentences in the correct order, and then write the conversation.

ADDITIONAL RESOURCES

At the back of the Workbook, you will find:
- Writing Practice
- Audio Script
- Answer Key

ORIENTATION

The Workbook, like the Student Book, includes an orientation for students. Before the students use the Workbook for the first time, direct them to To the Student on the next page. Go through the questions and tips with the students and answer any questions they may have so they can get the most out of using the Workbook.

LEARN ABOUT YOUR BOOK

A Look in the back of your book. Write the page number for this section.

Writing Practice ___   Audio Script ___   Answer Key ___

B Look at page 160. Find *answers will vary*. What does *answers will vary* mean?

C Where is the audio?

D Look at page 4. What does ▶ mean?

TIPS FOR USING THE AUDIO

Read the tips for using the audio.

- For all exercises, listen to each track many times.
- For dictation exercises, use the pause button so you can have more time to write.
- After you finish the unit, play the audio again and read the audio script in the back of the book at the same time.
- Also, for more listening practice, listen to the conversations and readings when you are in the car or on the bus.

WRITING TIPS

Read the writing tips.

- Start sentences with a capital letter.
- End statements with a period (.).
- End questions with a question mark (?).

For example:

My name is Jack.

What's your name?

Unit 1: Nice to Meet You

Lesson 1: Introduce Yourself

A Look at the map. Write the countries. Use the words in the box.

South Korea	Somalia	Haiti	~~Canada~~
El Salvador	Vietnam	Peru	Cambodia
the United States	Syria	Mexico	China

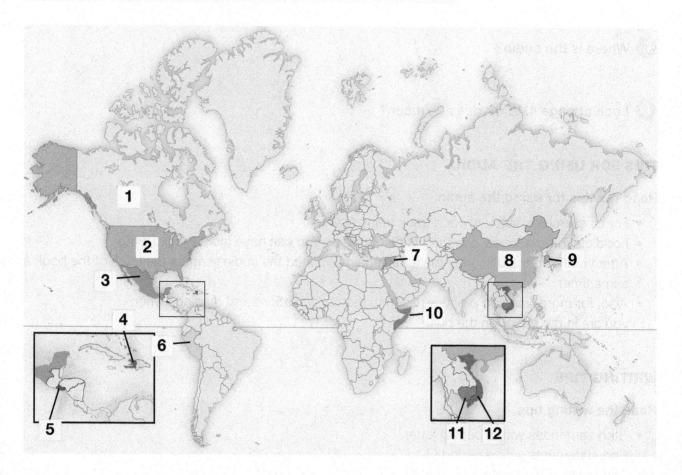

1. _____Canada_____   5. _____   9. _____

2. _____   6. _____   10. _____

3. _____   7. _____   11. _____

4. _____   8. _____   12. _____

B Look at the pictures. Write the names and the countries

1.

Maria / El Salvador

A: What's your name?

B: My name is _____ *Maria* _____.

A: Where are you from?

B: I'm from _____ *El Salvador* _____.

2.

Rosa / Haiti

A: What's your name?

B: My name is _____.

A: Where are you from?

B: I'm from _____.

3.

Teng / China

A: What's your name?

B: My name is _____.

A: Where are you from?

B: I'm from _____.

C Complete the conversation. Write your name and your native country.

A: What's your name?

B: My name is _____.

A: Where are you from?

B: I'm from _____.

Lesson 2: Spell First and Last Names

A Write capital letters.

A B _C_ D E _F_ G ___ I ___ ___ L M N O ___ ___ R ___ T U ___ W ___ ___ Z

B Write lower-case letters.

a _b_ c ___ e f g h ___ j k ___ ___ n ___ p q ___ s ___ u v ___ x y ___

C ▶ Listen. Write the names.

1. First name: _H_ _O_ _N_ _G_

Last name: _C_ _H_ _E_ _N_

2. First name: ___ ___ ___ ___

Last name: ___ ___ ___ ___ ___

3. First name: ___ ___ ___ ___

Last name: ___ ___ ___ ___ ___

4. First name: ___ ___ ___ ___

Last name: ___ ___ ___ ___

D Write your name.

First name: _____

Last name: _____

Lesson 3: Say and Write Important Numbers

A Read the words. Write the numbers. Use the numbers in the box.

0 1 2 3 4 5 6 7 8 9

1. three _3_

2. one ____

3. eight ____

4. six ____

5. four ____

6. nine ____

7. five ____

8. zero ____

9. seven ____

10. two ____

B ▶ Listen. Write the student ID numbers.

1. _5_ _3_ _6_ _9_ _1_

2. ____ ____ ____ ____ ____

3. ____ ____ ____ ____ ____

4. ____ ____ ____ ____ ____

> Student
>
> Name: Kim Chong
> ID Number: 53691
>
> Identification Card

C ▶ Listen. Write the telephone numbers.

1. _6_ _7_ _4_ - _5_ _5_ _5_ - _5_ _8_ _3_ _1_

2. ____ ____ ____ - _5_ _5_ _5_ - ____ ____ ____ ____

3. ____ ____ ____ - _5_ _5_ _5_ - ____ ____ ____ ____

4. ____ ____ ____ - _5_ _5_ _5_ - ____ ____ ____ ____

5. ____ ____ ____ - _5_ _5_ _5_ - ____ ____ ____ ____

6. ____ ____ ____ - _5_ _5_ _5_ - ____ ____ ____ ____

Lesson 4: Talk About Yourself

A Write *am* or *are*.

1. I ____am____ David Green.

2. You _____ a good teacher.

3. You _____ from Peru.

4. I _____ in the classroom.

5. You _____ a good student.

6. I _____ your English teacher.

7. You _____ my classmate.

8. I _____ from China.

B Write *I* or *You*.

1. ____You____ are Abdi Hassan.

2. _____ am from Somalia.

3. _____ am a new student.

4. _____ are the teacher.

5. _____ am from the United States.

6. _____ are a student.

7. _____ are in the library.

8. _____ am your classmate.

C Rewrite the sentences in Exercise B. Use *I'm* or *You're*.

1. You're Abdi Hassan. _____

2. _____

3. _____

4. _____

5. _____

6. _____

7. _____

8. _____

Lesson 5: Introduce Someone

A Look at the pictures. Complete the sentences. Write *He* or *She*.

1. ___*She*___ is from Peru.

2. _____ is from Syria.

3. _____ is from Somalia.

4. _____ is from Canada.

B Match the same sentences.

1. She is from China.	_f_	a. She's in the classroom.
2. He is a student.	___	b. She's working.
3. He is from Mexico.	___	c. He's a student.
4. She is in the classroom.	___	d. He's not here.
5. She is working.	___	e. He's from Mexico.
6. He is not here.	___	f. She's from China.

C ▶ Listen for *She's* or *He's*. Circle *a* or *b*.

1. a. She's   **b.** He's   **5. a.** She's   **b.** He's

2. a. She's   **b.** He's   **6. a.** She's   **b.** He's

3. a. She's   **b.** He's   **7. a.** She's   **b.** He's

4. a. She's   **b.** He's   **8. a.** She's   **b.** He's

D Write three sentences for each picture. Use *He is*, *She is*, *He's* or *She's*.

1.

Lin / my classmate

Lin is my classmate.

She is my classmate.

She's my classmate.

2.

Marco / from Peru

3.

Eva / my friend

4.

Akra / from Cambodia

Lesson 6: Talk About People

A Look at the pictures. Complete the sentences. Write *is* or *are*.

1. He ___is___ a teacher.

2. They _____ my classmates.

3. She _____ from China.

4. They _____ from the United States.

5. Jan and Tom _____ teachers.

6. Michael _____ a student.

7. Annette _____ from Haiti.

8. Eric and Tania _____ good students.

B ► Listen for *They're*, *We're*, and *You're*. Circle *a*, *b*, or *c*.

1. (a.) They're   b. We're   c. You're

2. a. They're   b. We're   c. You're

3. a. They're   b. We're   c. You're

4. a. They're   b. We're   c. You're

5. a. They're   b. We're   c. You're

6. a. They're   b. We're   c. You're

C Write sentences. Use *You're*, *We're*, or *They're*.

1. Lee and Tong are from Vietnam.   *They're from Vietnam.*

2. Carlos and I are new students. _____

3. You and Marta are my friends. _____

4. Rafal and Dora are classmates. _____

5. You and Mr. Santos are good teachers. _____

6. Barbara and I are from Canada. _____

7. Ms. Li and Mr. Green are friends. _____

8. You and Marco are good students. _____

9. Sara and I are friends. _____

10. Jin and Sung are from South Korea. _____

11. Dan and I are in the library. _____

12. You and Ana are classmates. _____

Lesson 7: Life Skills: Read and Fill Out a Form

A Read the sentences.

1. My first name is Marie.

2. My middle name is Anne.

3. My last name is Miller.

4. I'm from Canada.

5. My area code is 214.

6. My phone number is 555-5301.

7. My student ID number is 67920.

B Read the sentences again. Fill out the form.

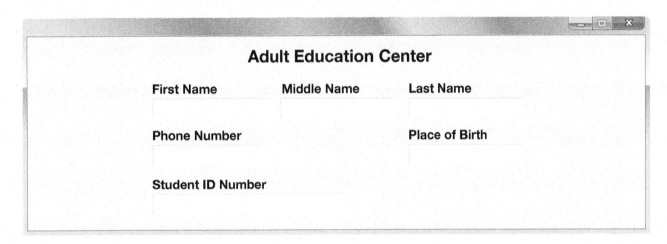

Adult Education Center

First Name	Middle Name	Last Name

Phone Number		Place of Birth

Student ID Number

Lesson 8: Read and Write About Greetings

A ▶ Listen to the story. Number the sentences in the correct order.

___ Other students say hello and kiss.

_1_ This is Ivan. He is a student.

___ Some students say hello and hug.

___ He says hello to his classmates and smiles.

___ Some students say hello and bow.

___ Some students say hello and shake hands.

B Read the sentences in Exercise A again. Write the sentences in the correct order.

This is Ivan. He is a student.

_____

_____

_____

_____

_____

C ▶ Listen again to check your answers to Exercise B.

Lesson 9: English at Work: Say Hello

A Number the sentences in the correct order.

___ **Sam:** Can I help you?

___ **Customer:** Thank you.

_1_ **Sam:** Welcome to Buy Best.

___ **Customer:** No, thank you. I'm fine.

B Read the sentences in Exercise A again. Write the sentences in the correct order.

Sam: _Welcome to Buy Best._____

Customer: _____

Sam: _____

Customer: _____

Unit 2: Welcome to class

Lesson 1: Ask for Things in Class

A Match the pictures with the words.

a.

b.

c.

d.

e.

f.

g.

h.

i.

1. a notebook ___b___

2. a book _____

3. a pencil _____

4. a dictionary app _____

5. a piece of paper _____

6. an eraser _____

7. a pen _____

8. a phone _____

9. a backpack _____

B ▶ Listen. Circle the correct pictures. Circle *a* or *b*.

1. a.   (b.)

2. a.   b.

3. a.   b.

4. a.   b.

5. a.   b.

C Read the conversations.. Write *I do* or *I don't*.

1. **A:** Do you have a pencil?

   B: Yes, _I do_____.

2. **A:** Do you have a dictionary app?

   B: No, _____.

3. **A:** Do you have a pen?

   B: Yes, _____.

4. **A:** Do you have a notebook?

   B: No, _____.

5. **A:** Do you have an eraser?

   B: Yes, _____.

Lesson 2: Follow Classroom Instructions

A Look at the pictures. Complete the instructions. Use the words in the box.

Turn on   Turn off   Open

Take out   Close   Put away

1. ___Turn on___ the light.

2. _____ your pencil.

3. _____ your book.

4. _____ your book.

5. _____ your book.

6. _____ the light.

B Read the test directions.

TEST DIRECTIONS

1. Put away your books. Don't use a dictionary app.

2. Use a pencil. Don't use a pen.

3. Turn off your phone.

C Read the test directions again. Circle *Yes* or *No*.

1. Put away your books.	(Yes)	No
2. Use a dictionary app.	Yes	No
3. Use a pencil.	Yes	No
4. Use a pen.	Yes	No
5. Turn off your phone.	Yes	No

D Write negative sentences.

1. Close your book.   *Don't close your book.* _____

2. Use a pencil.   _____

3. Turn on the light.   _____

4. Take out your notebook.   _____

5. Open the door.   _____

6. Put away your phone.   _____

Lesson 3: Talk About Places in a School

A Look at the pictures. Complete the words.

1. c_l_as_s_ro_o_m

2. re_T_tro_o_m

3. c_o_mput_e_r ___ab

4. _o_ff_e_ce

5. b_u_okstor_e_

6. t___s___ing roo___

7. l_a_b_e_ary

8. caf_e_teri_a_

B ▶ Listen. Choose the correct pictures. Circle *a* or *b*.

1. (a.) b.

2. a. b.

3. a. b.

4. a. b.

5. a. b.

6. a. b.

Lesson 4: Describe Locations

A Look at the map. Write *next to* or *across from*.

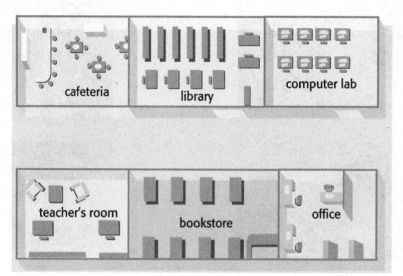

1. A: Where is the library? **B:** It's _____next to_____ the computer lab.

2. A: Where is the bookstore? **B:** It's _____ the office.

3. A: Where is the teacher's room? **B:** It's _____ the cafeteria.

4. A: Where is the office? **B:** It's _____ the computer lab.

5. A: Where is the library? **B:** It's _____ the cafeteria.

6. A: Where is the computer lab? **B:** It's _____ the library.

B Write sentences about the places in your school. Use *next to* or *across from*.

1. (computer lab) _The computer lab is across from the office._

2. (library) _____

3. (restroom) _____

4. (office) _____

5. (cafeteria) _____

6. (classroom) _____

Lesson 5: Life Skills: Understand a Form

A Read the form.

Vista Learning Center

○ Mr.
○ Mrs.
● Miss
○ Ms.

Last Name
Wang

First Name
Hong

Place of Birth
China

● Female ○ Male

Class
English 101

Teacher
Mrs. Smith

B Read the form again. Circle *Yes* or *No*.

1. Hong is from China.	(Yes)	No
2. Hong is single.	Yes	No
3. Hong is a woman.	Yes	No
4. Hong is in English 200.	Yes	No
5. Mrs. Smith is a man.	Yes	No
6. Mrs. Smith is Hong's teacher.	Yes	No

C Fill out the form. Use your information.

Vista Learning Center

○ Mr.
○ Mrs.
○ Miss
○ Ms.

Last Name

First Name

Place of Birth

○ Female ○ Male

Class

Teacher

Lesson 6: Talk about Study Skills

A Match the study skills with the pictures.

a.

b.

c.

d.

e.

f.

1. use a dictionary app ___c___

2. read signs _____

3. write new words _____

4. go to class _____

5. practice with my classmates _____

6. ask the teacher questions _____

B ▶ **Listen. Write the missing words.**

A: How do you study English?

B: I _____go_____ to class, and I _____ the teacher questions.

A: That's great!

B: How do you study English?

A: I _____ with my classmates. At home, I _____ in my notebook.

C **Cross out the incorrect verbs.**

1. I use / write a dictionary.

2. I go / read signs.

3. I study / go English at school.

4. I practice / talk to people.

5. I write / ask new words.

6. I ask / practice the teacher questions.

7. I go / use to the library.

8. I study / write in my notebook.

9. I practice / use with my classmates.

10. I talk / go to class.

D **How do *you* study English? Write your answer.**

I go to class, and I use a dictionary app.

_____

_____

_____

Lesson 7: Read and Write About Classrooms

A ▶ **Listen to the story. Number the sentences in the correct order.**

___ In her native country, students do not talk in class.

___ In the United States, students talk in groups.

___ The teacher listens to the students.

_1_ This is Lan.

___ They listen to the teacher.

___ Students ask questions.

B **Read the sentences in Exercise A again. Write the sentences in the correct order.**

This is Lan.

_____

_____

_____

_____

_____

C ▶ **Listen to the story again. Check your answers.**

Lesson 8: English at Work: Help Someone Fill Out a Form

A Number the sentences in the correct order.

___ **Student:** My first name is Rosa. My name is Rosa Sanchez.

___ **Alma:** Great! Write your first and last name on the form here.

_1_ **Alma:** What is your last name?

___ **Student:** My last name is Sanchez.

___ **Alma:** OK. What is your first name?

B Read the sentences in Exercise A again. Write the sentences in the correct order.

Alma: _What is your last name?_____

Student: _____

Alma: _____

Student: _____

Alma: _____

Unit 3: On Time

Lesson 1: Say the Time

A ▶ Listen for the number. Circle *a* or *b*.

1. a. 7   (b). 9

2. a. 18   b. 15

3. a. 23   b. 28

4. a. 36   b. 35

5. a. 44   b. 40

6. a. 52   b. 57

B Match the times with the clocks.

a.

b.

c.

d.

e.

f.

1. 6:10 __b__   3. 2:15 _____   5. 1:50 _____

2. 11:05 _____   4. 4:00 _____   6. 8:30 _____

C Look at the clocks. Write the time.

1. _____8:10_____

2. _____

3. _____

4. _____

5. _____

6. _____

D Look at the clocks again. Complete the conversations.

1. **A:** What time is it?

   B: _It's 8:10_____.

2. **A:** _____?

   B: It's 3:05.

3. **A:** What time is it?

   B: _____.

4. **A:** What time is it?

   B: _____.

5. **A:** What time is it?

   B: _____.

6. **A:** _____?

   B: It's 9:45.

Lesson 2: Talk About Schedules

A Complete the conversations. Use the words in the boxes.

| at | from | time | ~~What~~ |

1. **A:** ____What____ time is your English class?

   B: It's _____ 1:00 to 5:00.

   A: What _____ is your break?

   B: It's _____ 2:15.

| at | is | time | to |

2. **A:** What _____ is your English class?

   B: It's from 6:00 _____ 9:00.

   A: What time _____ your break?

   B: It's _____ 7:45.

B ▶ Listen for the time. Circle *a* or *b*.

1. a. 9:15　　　　　b. 9:50

2. a. 10:14　　　　b. 10:40

3. a. 12:13　　　　b. 12:30

4. a. 2:45　　　　　b. 2:40

C ▶ Listen. Write the times.

1. It's from ____9:15____ to ____1:15____.

2. It's from _____ to _____.

3. It's from _____ to _____.

4. It's from _____ to _____.

D Look at the sign. Circle *Yes* or *No*.

Place	From	To
Cafeteria	11:00 A.M.	1:30 P.M.
School	7:00 A.M.	7:00 P.M.
Computer lab	10:15 A.M.	3:45 P.M.
Office	7:30 A.M.	4:30 P.M.
Library	11:00 A.M.	5:30 P.M.
Bookstore	9:15 A.M.	12:00 P.M.

1. The cafeteria is open at 11:00 A.M.   (Yes)   No

2. The school is open from 7:00 A.M. to 8:30 P.M.   Yes   No

3. The computer lab is open at 10:00 A.M.   Yes   No

4. The office is open from 7:00 A.M. to 4:30 P.M.   Yes   No

5. The library is open at 3:30 P.M.   Yes   No

6. The bookstore is open from 9:15 A.M. to 12:00 P.M.   Yes   No

7. The school opens at 7:00 P.M.   Yes   No

8. The office closes at 4:30 P.M.   Yes   No

E Write sentences. Use *from / to* or *at*.

1. The library is open / 9:00   _The library is open at 9:00._

2. My break is / 2:00 / 2:20   _____

3. The cafeteria is open / 7:00 / 3:00   _____

4. My computer class starts / 4:30   _____

5. The office is open / 11:30   _____

6. My English class is / 10:00 / 12:00   _____

7. The computer lab is open / 8:00 / 11:00   _____

8. My break is over / 3:00   _____

Lesson 3: Talk About Daily Activities

A Match the pictures with the words.

 a.

 b.

 c.

 d.

 e.

 f.

 g.

 h.

 i.

1. go to sleep ___c___

2. get up _____

3. eat breakfast _____

4. take a shower _____

5. eat lunch _____

6. get dressed _____

7. go to school _____

8. go to work _____

9. get home _____

B Complete the sentences. Write the correct form of the verbs.

1. Clara **(go)** _____goes_____ to sleep at 9:00.

2. Ho-Jin **(take)** _____ a shower at 6:30.

3. Zara **(get)** _____ dressed at 8:00.

4. Salim **(eat)** _____ lunch at 12:30.

5. Liz **(get up)** _____ at 7:00.

6. Victor **(go)** _____ to work at 8:30.

C Read the daily activities. Write about yourself.

1. get up   _I get up at 7:00._____

2. take a shower   _____

3. get dressed   _____

4. eat breakfast   _____

5. go to work   _____

6. go to school   _____

7. get home   _____

D ▶ Listen for the daily activity. Circle *a* or *b*.

1. ⓐ goes to work   **b.** takes a shower

2. **a.** eats lunch   **b.** gets dressed

3. **a.** goes to sleep   **b.** goes to school

4. **a.** eats breakfast   **b.** eats lunch

5. **a.** gets up   **b.** gets home

Lesson 4: Talk about Your Weekly Schedule

A Complete the schedule. Write the days in the correct order. Use the words in the box.

Friday   Monday   Saturday   ~~Sunday~~   Thursday   Tuesday   Wednesday

Sunday	_____	_____	_____	_____	_____	_____
Work	Class	Work	Class	Work	Work	
8 – 4	11 – 3	8 – 4	11 – 3	8 – 4	10 – 2	

B ▶ Listen for the day. Circle *a* or *b*.

1. (a) Monday   b. Wednesday

2. a. Friday   b. Wednesday

3. a. Sunday   b. Saturday

4. a. Tuesday   b. Thursday

5. a. Saturday   b. Sunday

C Complete the sentences. Write *from / to* or *on*.

1. Paul works _____*from*_____ Monday _____*to*_____ Thursday.

2. Sun-Li goes to school _____ Friday.

3. Robert goes to the library _____ Saturday.

4. Anna studies English _____ 8:00 _____ 11:00 in the morning.

5. Ivan gets home late _____ Tuesday.

6. Kamila gets up at 6:30 _____ Tuesday _____ Friday.

D Read Mark's schedule.

Sunday	Monday	Tuesday	Wednesday	Thursday	Friday	Saturday
Soccer game 3:00 – 5:00	Work 9:00 – 5:00	Work 9:00 – 5:00	Work 8:00 – 4:00	Work 10:00 – 4:00	Work 2:00 – 9:00	Soccer practice 1:00 – 4:00
	English class 6:00 – 9:00	Soccer game 6:00 – 8:00	English class 6:00 – 9:00			

E Read Mark's schedule again. Circle *Yes* or *No*.

1. Mark has soccer games two days a week.	(Yes)	No
2. He goes to work three days a week.	Yes	No
3. He goes to work from 8:00 to 12:00 on Monday.	Yes	No
4. His English class starts at 3:00 on Monday.	Yes	No
5. Mark goes to English class two days a week.	Yes	No
6. He goes to the library on Thursday.	Yes	No
7. He plays soccer on Friday.	Yes	No
8. He doesn't go to work on Friday.	Yes	No

F Write your weekly schedule.

Sunday	Monday	Tuesday	Wednesday	Thursday	Friday	Saturday

Lesson 5: Life Skills: Read and Write a Weekly Schedule

A Read the numbers. Write the words.

1. 71 _____seventy-one_____

2. 59 _____

3. 11 _____

4. 60 _____

5. 33 _____

6. 14 _____

7. 100 _____

8. 90 _____

9. 47 _____

10. 86 _____

B ▶ Listen. Write the number.

1. ___93___

2. _____

3. _____

4. _____

5. _____

6. _____

7. _____

8. _____

C Read the schedule. Match the employees to their break time.

Last Name	First Name	6a	7a	8a	9a	10a	11a	12p	1p	2p	3p	4p	5p	6p
Diaz	Carlos				Work	Work	Break	Work	Work	Work	Work	Work	Work	
Stem	Jen		Work	Work	Work	Break	Work	Work	Work	Work	Work			
Solomon	John				Work	Work	Break	Work	Work	Work	Work	Work	Work	Work
Sun	Wen	Work	Work	Work	Break	Work	Work	Work	Work	Work				

■ Work
■ Break

1. Carlos Diaz ___c___

2. Jen Stem _____

3. John Solomon _____

4. Wen Sun _____

a. from 11:00 to 12:00

b. from 9:30 to 10:30

c. from 10:00 to 11:00

d. from 12:00 to 1:00

D Read the schedules. Complete the sentences.

Mai's Schedule
Class 9:00 A.M.–12:00 P.M.
Break 10:15 A.M.–10:30 A.M.

Dawit's Schedule
Class 6:00 P.M.–9:00 P.M.
Break 7:30 P.M.–7:50 P.M.

1. Mai's class is ____two____ hours.

2. Her break is _____ minutes.

3. Dawit's class is _____ hours.

4. His break is _____ minutes.

E Answer the questions about your schedule.

1. When do you work?

_____

_____

2. When do you go to English class?

_____

_____

3. When do you study?

_____

_____

F Complete your weekly schedule.

Lesson 6: Read and Write About Time

A ▶ Listen to the story. Number the sentences in the correct order.

___ He goes to school after work.

_1_ Manny gets up at 6:00.

___ Manny meets friends on Saturday.
But he is late!

___ He gets to work at 7:55. He starts work
at 8:00. He is on time.

___ He gets to class at 5:45. Class starts at
6:00. He is early.

B Read the sentences in Exercise A again. Write the sentences in the correct order.

Manny gets up at 6:00.

_____

_____

_____

_____

C ▶ Listen again. Check your answers in Exercise B.

Lesson 7: English at Work: Talk About Schedules

A Number the sentences in the correct order.

___ **Wei:** OK. Please call me next time.

___ **Employee:** I'm sorry!

_1_ **Wei:** It is 9:10. You're late.

___ **Employee:** The bus was late. I'm sorry.

___ **Wei:** Work starts at 9:00. Why are you late?

B Read the sentences in Exercise A again. Write the sentences in the correct order.

Wei: _It is 9:10. You're late._____

Employee: _____

Wei: _____

Employee: _____

Wei: _____

Lesson 1: Identify Family Members

A Look at the pictures. Circle *a* or *b*.

1. a. brother   b. sister

2. a. grandmother   b. grandfather

3. a. father   b. mother

4. a. daughter   b. son

5. a. children   b. parents

6. a. wife   b. husband

7. a. children   b. parents

8. a. grandfather   b. sister

B ► Listen. Write the missing words. Use the words in the box.

brother   daughter   ~~father~~   grandfather   grandmother

husband   mother   wife   sister   son

1. **A:** Who's that?

   B: That's my _father_____.

2. **A:** Who's that?

   B: That's my _____.

3. **A:** Who's that?

   B: That's my _____.

4. **A:** Who's that?

   B: That's my _____.

5. **A:** Who's that?

   B: That's my _____.

6. **A:** Who's that?

   B: That's my _____.

7. **A:** Who's that?

   B: That's my _____.

8. **A:** Who's that?

   B: That's my _____.

9. **A:** Who's that?

   B: That's my _____.

10. **A:** Who's that?

    B: That's my _____.

Lesson 2: Say Who Is in Your Family

A Read the story.

This is Abdel and his family. His wife is Asha. Abdel and Asha have two sons. Their names are Omar and Mahad. They have one daughter. Her name is Zola.

B Read the story again. Circle *a* or *b*.

1. Asha is Abdel's _____.

a. wife   b. daughter

2. Omar is Abdel's _____.

a. father   b. son

3. Asha is Omar's _____.

a. sister   b. mother

4. Mahad is Zola's _____.

a. brother   b. father

5. Abdel is Mahad's _____.

a. father   b. brother

6. Mahad is Omar's _____.

a. father   b. brother

7. Zola is Asha's _____.

a. sister   b. daughter

8. Abdel is Zola's _____.

a. father   b. son

C Answer the questions about your family. Circle *Yes* or *No*.

1. Do you have any sisters?   Yes   No

2. Do you have any brothers?   Yes   No

3. Do you have any children?   Yes   No

D Complete the chart. Use the words in the box.

brother	parents	daughters	sister	brothers
child	grandparent	son	parent	daughter
grandparents	children	sisters	sons	

Singular	Plural
parent	*parents*

E Complete the sentences. Use the words in the box.

brothers   children   grandparents   parents   sisters

1. My sister Pam and my sister Meg are my _____*sisters*_____.

2. My mother and my father are my _____.

3. My grandmother and my grandfather are my _____.

4. My brother David and my brother Adam are my _____.

5. My son and my daughter are my _____.

Lesson 3: Talk About Chores at Home

A Look at the pictures. Write the household chores. Use the words in the box.

wash the dishes	make dinner	take out the garbage
do the laundry	clean the house	~~vacuum~~

1. _____ *vacuum* _____

2. _____

3. _____

4. _____

5. _____

6. _____

B Write the questions. Complete the answers. Use the verbs in parentheses.

1. (vacuum)

   A: _Do you vacuum_____?

   B: Yes, _I do_____.

2. (make dinner)

   A: _____?

   B: No, _____.

3. (clean the house)

   A: _____?

   B: Yes, _____.

4. (wash the dishes)

   A: _____?

   B: No, _____.

5. (take out the garbage)

   A: _____?

   B: Yes, _____.

6. (do the laundry)

   A: _____?

   B: No, _____.

C Look at the chores. Check the ones you do at home.

❑   clean the house   ❑   take out the garbage

❑   do the laundry   ❑   wash the dishes

❑   make dinner   ❑   vacuum

Lesson 4: Say Months of the Year

A Write the months in order. Use the words in the box.

April	August	December	February	~~January~~	July
June	March	May	November	October	September

1. _____January_____   7. _____

2. _____   8. _____

3. _____   9. _____

4. _____   10. _____

5. _____   11. _____

6. _____   12. _____

B ▶ Listen for the ordinal number. Circle *a* or *b*.

1. a. first   (b.) second

2. a. seventh   b. seventeenth

3. a. fifth   b. fifteenth

4. a. eighth   b. eighteenth

5. a. twenty-second   b. twenty-seventh

6. a. thirteenth   b. thirtieth

Lesson 5: Write Dates

A Write the number or the month.

Number	Month	Number	Month
_1_	January	_____	July
2	_February_	_____	August
3	_____	9	_____
4	_____	10	_____
_____	May	_____	November
6	_____	12	_____

B Match the dates.

1. October 31, 2000   _f_   a. 12/25/82

2. July 4, 1990   _____   b. 2/14/06

3. December 25, 1982   _____   c. 3/17/74

4. February 14, 2006   _____   d. 7/4/90

5. March 17, 1974   _____   e. 11/21/95

6. May 27, 1950   _____   f. 10/31/00

7. September 30, 2010   _____   g. 4/7/19

8. November 21, 1995   _____   h. 5/27/50

9. April 7, 2019   _____   i. 6/10/25

10. June 10, 2025   _____   j. 9/30/10

C Write the dates.

1. April 14, 1998   _4/14/98_

2. June 17, 1985   _____

3. September 1, 2007   _____

4. February 22, 1974   _____

5. March 21, 2010   _____

6. _____   11/29/19

7. _____   7/13/22

8. _____   2/8/95

9. _____   10/19/68

10. _____   5/31/83

D Circle the month, day, or year.

1. Circle the month.   ⑥/20/93

2. Circle the day.   9/30/04

3. Circle the year.   12/6/72

4. Circle the month.   5/30/06

5. Circle the day.   10/17/58

6. Circle the year.   1/9/08

7. Circle the month.   2/25/18

8. Circle the day.   11/4/97

9. Circle the year.   4/2/03

> 4/8/05 = **month**
>
> 4/8/05 = **day**
>
> 4/8/**05** = **year**

Lesson 6: Life Skills: Fill Out a form

A Read the sentences about Ji-yoo.

1. My first name is Ji-yoo.

2. My last name is Lee.

3. I'm from Korea.

4. I was born on June 1, 1956.

5. I'm in ESL 2.

6. I go to English class on Tuesday and Thursday.

7. My teacher's name is Mrs. Baca.

8. My class is from 2:00 to 5:00.

9. My class is in Room 12.

B Read the sentences again. Fill out the form for Ji-yoo.

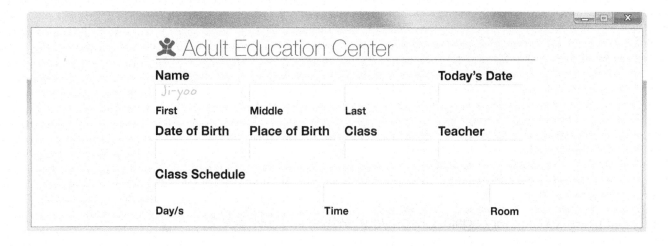

⚉ Adult Education Center

Name			Today's Date
Ji-yoo			
First	Middle	Last	
Date of Birth	Place of Birth	Class	Teacher

Class Schedule

Day/s	Time	Room

Lesson 7: Read and Write About Home and Work

A ▶ Listen to the story. Number the sentences in the correct order.

___ In their native country, men go to work.

___ They both do household chores. Lucas washes the dishes.

___ Lucas goes to the supermarket, too.

_1_ Lucas and Carla are married. Lucas is Carla's husband. Carla is Lucas's wife.

___ In their native country, women do the household chores.

___ In the United States, Carla and Lucas go to work.

B Read the sentences in Exercise A again. Write the sentences in the correct order.

Lucas and Carla are married. Lucas is Carla's husband. Carla is Lucas's wife.

_____

_____

_____

_____

_____

C ▶ Listen to the story again. Check your answers to Exercise B.

Lesson 8: English at Work: Ask About Someone's Family

Mara

Coworker

A Number the sentences in the correct order.

___ **Coworker:** Yes, it is. That's my brother and three sisters.

_1_ **Mara:** Is that your family?

___ **Mara:** Who's that?

___ **Coworker:** That's my grandmother.

___ **Coworker:** Thank you!

___ **Mara:** You have a nice family.

B Read the sentences in Exercise A again. Write the sentences in the correct order.

Mara: _Is that your family?_ _____

Coworker: _____

Mara: _____

Coworker: _____

Mara: _____

Coworker: _____

Unit 5: How Much Is It?

Lesson 1: Make Change with U.S. Coins

A Match the pictures with the words.

a.

b.

c.

d.

e.

1. a dime ___b___   **4.** a penny _____

2. a quarter _____   **5.** a half-dollar _____

3. a nickel _____

B Read the words. Write the coins. Use the words in the box.

| a dime | a half-dollar | a nickel | a quarter |

1. two dimes and one nickel = _____*a quarter*_____

2. five pennies = _____

3. two quarters = _____

4. five pennies and one nickel = _____

5. one quarter, two dimes, and one nickel = _____

C Look at the pictures. Complete the conversations.

1. **A:** Do you have change for a dollar?

    B: Yes. I have a _____quarter_____, six

    _____dimes_____, and three

    _____nickels_____.

2. **A:** Do you have change for a quarter?

    B: Yes. I have two _____ and

    a _____.

3. **A:** Do you have change for a dollar?

    B: Yes. I have three _____,

    two _____, and

    a _____.

4. **A:** Do you have change for a quarter?

    B: Yes. I have four _____ and

    five _____.

5. **A:** Do you have change for a dollar?

    B: Yes. I have two _____ and five

    _____.

Lesson 2: Make Change with U.S. Bills

A Look at the pictures. Write the amount. Use the words in the box.

fifty   five   ~~one~~   one hundred   ten   twenty

1. _____one_____ dollar

2. _____ dollars

3. _____ dollars

4. _____ dollars

5. _____ dollars

6. _____ dollars

B Look at the pictures. Write the amount. Use the words in the box.

fifty dollars   one hundred dollars   ten dollars   ~~twenty dollars~~

1. _____ *twenty dollars* _____

2. _____

3. _____

4. _____

C ▶ Listen. Write the missing words.

1. **A:** Do you have change for a ___*five*___?

   B: Yes. I have five ___*ones*___.

2. **A:** Do you have change for a _____?

   B: Yes. I have a twenty and three _____.

3. **A:** Do you have change for a _____?

   B: Yes. I have a _____ and five ones.

4. **A:** Do you have change for a _____?

   B: Yes. I have a fifty, a _____, and three tens.

Lesson 3: Ask Where Things Are in a Store

A Look at the pictures. Write the words. Use the words in the box.

aspirin	batteries	deodorant	light bulbs
paper towels	razors	shampoo	shaving cream
soap	tissues	toilet paper	~~toothpaste~~

1. _____toothpaste_____

2. _____

3. _____

4. _____

5. _____

6. _____

7. _____

8. _____

9. _____

10. _____

11. _____

12. _____

B Complete the questions. Write *is* or *are*.

1. Where ____is____ the toilet paper?

2. Where _____ the razors?

3. Where _____ the deodorant?

4. Where _____ the toothpaste?

5. Where _____ the light bulbs?

6. Where _____ the paper towels?

7. Where _____ the shaving cream?

8. Where _____ the shampoo?

C Complete the questions. Write *Where is* or *Where are*.

1. A: Excuse me. _____Where is_____ the soap?

B: Aisle 2.

2. A: Excuse me. _____ the tissues?

B: Aisle 3.

3. A: Excuse me. _____ the batteries?

B: It's in Aisle 1.

4. A: Excuse me. _____ the toilet paper?

B: Aisle 4.

5. A: Excuse me. _____ the aspirin?

B: It's in Aisle 5.

Lesson 4: Ask for and Say Prices

A Look at the pictures. Circle *a* or *b*.

1. ⓐ $5.76   **b.** $5.56

2. a. $13.10   **b.** $13.20

3. a. $25.14   **b.** $25.12

4. a. $60.30   **b.** $65.30

5. a. $100.05   **b.** $100.10

B ▶ Listen. Write the prices.

1. _____   **4.** _____

2. _____   **5.** _____

3. _____   **6.** _____

C ▶ Listen. Write the prices.

1. _____

2. _____

3. _____

4. _____

5. _____

6. _____

D ▶ Listen. Write the prices.

1.

2.

3.

4.

5.

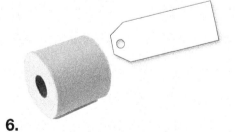

6.

Lesson 5: Life Skills: Read a Receipt

A Read the receipt.

Family Drugstore

Date> 3/4/19

1 Shampoo	
1 Soap	$5.79
1 Tissues	2.99
1 Razors	3.79
1 Shaving cream	5.99
1 Batteries	6.25
	6.99

Transaction Total:

6 items	Subtotal	$31.80
	Tax	2.23
	Total	$34.03

Paid by: Credit card $34.03

B Read the receipt again. Circle *Yes* or *No*.

1. The name of the store is City Drugstore.	Yes	(No)
2. The date of the receipt is April 3, 2018.	Yes	No
3. The batteries are $6.99.	Yes	No
4. The subtotal is $34.03.	Yes	No
5. The person is paying with cash.	Yes	No

C Read the receipt again. Write the prices.

1. How much are the razors? _$5.99_

2. How much is the soap? _____

3. How much are the tissues? _____

4. How much is the shampoo? _____

5. How much are the batteries? _____

6. How much is the shaving cream? _____

D Look at the pictures. What do you see? Use the words in the box.

a card   enter your PIN   ~~insert your card~~   remove your card

sign your name   swipe your card   tap OK

1. ___*insert your card*___

2. _____

3. _____

4. _____

5. _____

6. _____

7. _____

Lesson 6: Read and Write About Shopping

A ▶ Listen to the story. Number the sentences in the correct order.

___ She is happy.

_1_ This is Edna. In her native country, she shops at a market.

___ Edna pays a good price in the United States, too. She buys things on sale.

___ Each item has one price.

___ She talks about the price. She asks for a better price.

___ In the United States, Edna shops in a big store.

B Read the sentences in Exercise A again. Write the sentences in the correct order.

This is Edna. In her native country, she shops at a market.

_____

_____

_____

_____

_____

C ▶ Listen to the story again. Check your answers to Exercise B.

Lesson 7: English at Work: Answer a Customer's Questions

A Number the sentences in the correct order.

___ **Fatima:** The total is $4.95.

___ **Customer:** OK. I need new batteries.

_1_ **Customer:** Excuse me. How much are the batteries?

___ **Fatima:** Yes, I do.

___ **Fatima:** Let me see. They're $4.79.

___ **Customer:** Do you have change for a ten?

___ **Customer:** Great. Here you go.

___ **Fatima:** Thank you. Here is your change.

B Read the sentences in Exercise A again. Write the sentences in the correct order.

Customer: _Excuse me. How much are the batteries?_____

Fatima: _____

Customer: _____

Fatima: _____

Customer: _____

Fatima: _____

Customer: _____

Fatima: _____

Unit 6: Let's Eat

Lesson 1: Talk About Vegetables

A Look at the pictures. Write the vegetables. Use the words in the box.

> onions   carrots   lettuce   peppers   potatoes
>
> tomatoes   cucumbers   mushrooms   peas

1. _tomatoes_   2. _____   3. _____

4. _____   5. _____   6. _____

7. _____   8. _____   9. _____

B ▶ Listen for the vegetables. Circle *a* or *b*.

1. a. tomatoes and onions   b. potatoes and onions

2. a. peppers and mushrooms   b. peas and mushrooms

3. a. carrots and lettuce   b. cucumbers and lettuce

4. a. potatoes and peppers   b. potatoes and peas

C Read the story.

Sandra needs to make dinner. She wants to make chicken and vegetables. She has chicken, onions, and peas. She needs potatoes, carrots, and mushrooms. Her son goes to the store. He buys the vegetables. Sandra makes dinner. It's delicious!

D Read the story again. Complete the sentences. Circle *a* or *b*.

1. Sandra wants to make _____.

   a. lunch

   b. dinner

2. She wants to make _____.

   a. chicken and carrots

   b. chicken and vegetables

3. She has chicken, _____, and peas.

   a. mushrooms

   b. onions

4. Sandra needs potatoes, carrots, and _____.

   a. mushrooms

   b. onions

5. Her _____ goes to the store.

   a. husband

   b. son

6. He buys _____.

   a. potatoes, carrots, and mushrooms

   b. potatoes, carrots, and onions

Lesson 2: Say What You Like and Don't Like

A Look at the pictures. Complete the sentences. Cross out *like* or *don't like*.
Use the words in the box.

carrots   cucumbers   lettuce   onions

peas   ~~peppers~~   ~~potatoes~~   tomatoes

1. I like / ~~don't like~~ _____*potatoes*_____. I ~~like~~ / don't like _____*peppers*_____.

2. I like / don't like _____. I like / don't like _____.

3. I like / don't like _____. I like / don't like _____.

4. I like / don't like _____. I like / don't like _____.

B ▶ Listen. Write the vegetables.

1. **A:** Do you like vegetables?

   B: I like _____peas_____. I don't like _____onions_____.

2. **A:** Do you like vegetables?

   B: I like _____. I don't like _____.

3. **A:** Do you like vegetables?

   B: I like _____. I don't like _____.

4. **A:** Do you like vegetables?

   B: I like _____. I don't like _____.

C Answer the questions about yourself. Circle *Yes* or *No*. Then write a sentence.

1. Do you like peas?   (Yes)   No

   _I like peas._____

2. Do you like lettuce?   Yes   No

   _____

3. Do you like carrots?   Yes   No

   _____

4. Do you like peppers?   Yes   No

   _____

5. Do you like mushrooms?   Yes   No

   _____

6. Do you like potatoes?   Yes   No

   _____

7. Do you like onions?   Yes   No

   _____

Lesson 3: Say What Someone Likes and Doesn't Like

A Look at the pictures. Write the fruits. Use the words in the box.

apples   bananas   cherries   grapes   mangoes

oranges   peaches   pears   strawberries

1. _____apples_____   2. _____   3. _____

4. _____   5. _____   6. _____

7. _____   8. _____   9. _____

B Read the conversations. Complete the answers.

1. **A:** Does Tom like bananas?

   B: Yes. He _____ likes _____ bananas.

2. **A:** Does Maria like strawberries?

   B: Yes. She _____ strawberries.

3. **A:** Does Dek like peaches?

   B: No. He _____ peaches.

4. **A:** Does Meg like cherries?

   B: Yes. She _____ cherries.

5. **A:** Does Pam like grapes?

   B: No. She _____ grapes.

6. **A:** Does Tom like pears?

   B: No. He _____ pears.

C Look at the pictures. Complete the sentences. Use *like* and *doesn't like*.

1. Kim _____ likes grapes _____.

2. Yen _____.

3. Roberto's sister _____.

4. Eva _____.

5. My father _____.

6. My teacher _____.

Lesson 4: Ask What Someone Needs

A Look at the pictures. What do you see? Use the words in the box.

a bag of rice	a box of cereal	~~a can of soup~~
a dozen eggs	a gallon of milk	a loaf of bread

1. _____a can of soup_____

2. _____

3. _____

4. _____

5. _____

6. _____

B Complete the conversations. Write the plural form of the words in the parentheses.

1. **A:** What do we need from the store?

    B: We need two **(gallon)** _____gallons_____ of milk and two **(box)** _____ of cereal.

2. **A:** What do we need from the store?

    B: We need four **(pound)** _____ of chicken and three **(bag)** _____

    of rice.

3. **A:** What do we need from the store?

    B: We need two **(loaf)** _____ of bread and three **(box)** _____ of cereal.

4. **A:** What do we need from the store?

    B: We need three **(pound)** _____ of fish and five **(can)** _____ of soup.

C Look at the pictures. Complete the conversations.

1. **A:** Do you need anything from the store?

    B: Yes. I need a _____loaf of bread_____

    and two _____gallons of milk_____.

2. **A:** Do you need anything from the store?

    B: Yes. I need a _____

    and two _____.

3. **A:** Do you need anything from the store?

    B: Yes. I need two _____

    and three _____.

4. **A:** Do you need anything from the store?

    B: Yes. I need a _____

    and two _____.

Lesson 5: Life Skills: Read an Ad

A Read the ad.

Shop Mart Weekly Specials

Loaf of bread $1.79

One dozen eggs $1.29

Chicken $1.99/lb.

Tomato soup 79¢
Buy one, get one free

Cereal $4.25

Bananas 49¢/lb.

B Read the ad again. Write the prices.

1. How much is a loaf of bread? $1.79

2. How much is three pounds of chicken? _____

3. How much are four cans of soup? _____

4. How much is a box of cereal? _____

5. How much are two dozen eggs? _____

6. How much is a pound of bananas? _____

C Look at the pictures. Write a shopping list.

1 gallon of milk
_____
_____
_____
_____

Lesson 6: Read a Menu and Order Food

A Match the pictures with the words.

 a.

 b.

 c.

 d.

 e.

 f.

1. fruit salad _____d_____

2. pancakes _____

3. cereal _____

4. eggs and toast _____

5. juice _____

6. tea _____

B ▶ Listen for the menu items. Circle *a* or *b*.

1. (a)   b.

2. a.   b.

3. a.   b.

4. a.   b.

Lesson 7: Read and Write About Eating

A ▶ **Listen to the story. Number the sentences in the correct order.**

___ Many children eat with their hands.

___ This is Riko. In her native country, many people drink soup.

_1_ This is Tran. In his native country, most people eat with chopsticks.

___ In the United States, most people eat with a fork, knife, and spoon.

___ They eat sandwiches and French fries with their hands.

B **Read the sentences in Exercise A again. Write the sentences in the correct order.**

This is Tran. In his native country, most people eat with chopsticks.

_____

_____

_____

_____

C ▶ **Listen to the story again. Check your answers to Exercise B.**

Lesson 8: English at Work: Do an Inventory

A Number the sentences in the correct order.

___ **Carlos:** OK, got it! What about vegetables? What do we need?

___ **Sara:** Oh! We need three gallons of milk!

_1_ **Carlos:** Do we need ground beef?

___ **Carlos:** Anything else?

___ **Sara:** Yes, we need four pounds of ground beef.

___ **Sara:** Let's see. We need carrots, potatoes, and lettuce.

B Read the sentences in Exercise A again. Write the sentences in the correct order.

Carlos: _Do we need ground beef?_ _____

Sara: _____

Carlos: _____

Sara: _____

Carlos: _____

Sara: _____

Unit 7: Apartment for Rent

Lesson 1: Identify Rooms in a Home

A Look at the pictures. Write the rooms. Use the words in the box.

closet	bathroom	~~bedroom~~	dining room
garage	kitchen	laundry room	living room

1. _____bedroom_____

2. _____

3. _____

4. _____

5. _____

6. _____

7. _____

8. _____

B Look at the apartment. Complete the conversation.

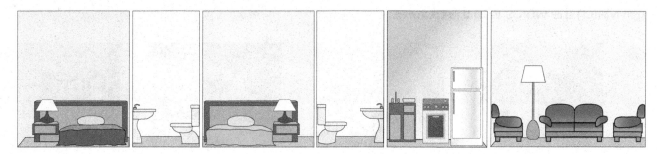

A: Guess what? I have a new apartment.

B: Really? What's it like?

A: It has two ___bedrooms___, two _____, a _____, and a _____.

B: It sounds great!

C Read the story.

My name is Sahra. I have a new apartment. It has two bedrooms, one bathroom, a living room, and a kitchen. It's great!

D Read the story again. Circle *Yes* or *No*.

1. Sahra has an old apartment.	Yes	No
2. The apartment has two bedrooms.	Yes	No
3. It has a living room.	Yes	No
4. It has a dining room.	Yes	No
5. It has a kitchen.	Yes	No
6. It has a laundry room.	Yes	No
7. It has two bathrooms	Yes	No
8. It has a basement.	Yes	No

Lesson 2: Talk About a Home

A Match the words with the pictures.

a.   b.   c.   d.

1. sunny ____c____   **2.** new _____   **3.** large _____   **4.** small _____

B ▶ Listen. Write the missing words.

1. **A:** Can you tell me about the apartment for rent?

   B: There is a _____sunny_____ living room and a _____ kitchen.

   A: It sounds nice.

2. **A:** Can you tell me about the apartment for rent?

   B: There is a _____ garage and a _____ dining room.

   A: It sounds nice.

3. **A:** Can you tell me about the apartment for rent?

   B: There is a _____ closet and a _____ basement.

   A: It sounds nice.

4. **A:** Can you tell me about the apartment for rent?

   B: There is a _____ bedroom and a _____ kitchen.

   A: It sounds nice.

5. **A:** Can you tell me about the apartment for rent?

   B: There is a _____ kitchen and a _____ bathroom.

   A: It sounds nice.

C Complete the sentences. Write *is* or *are*.

1. There _____is_____ one bedroom.

2. There _____ three closets.

3. There _____ a large kitchen.

4. There _____ a new bathroom.

5. There _____ four sunny bedrooms.

6. There _____ a large garage.

7. There _____ five bedrooms.

8. There _____ a laundry room.

9. There _____ two large bathrooms.

10. There _____ a small kitchen.

D Complete the sentences. Write *There is* or *There are*.

1. _____There is_____ a new kitchen.

2. _____ four bathrooms.

3. _____ a large living room.

4. _____ a large basement.

5. _____ two small bedrooms.

6. _____ a new dining room.

7. _____ six closets.

8. _____ a large laundry room.

9. _____ a sunny kitchen.

10. _____ four large closets.

Lesson 3: Ask About Furniture and Appliances

A Match the word to the picture.

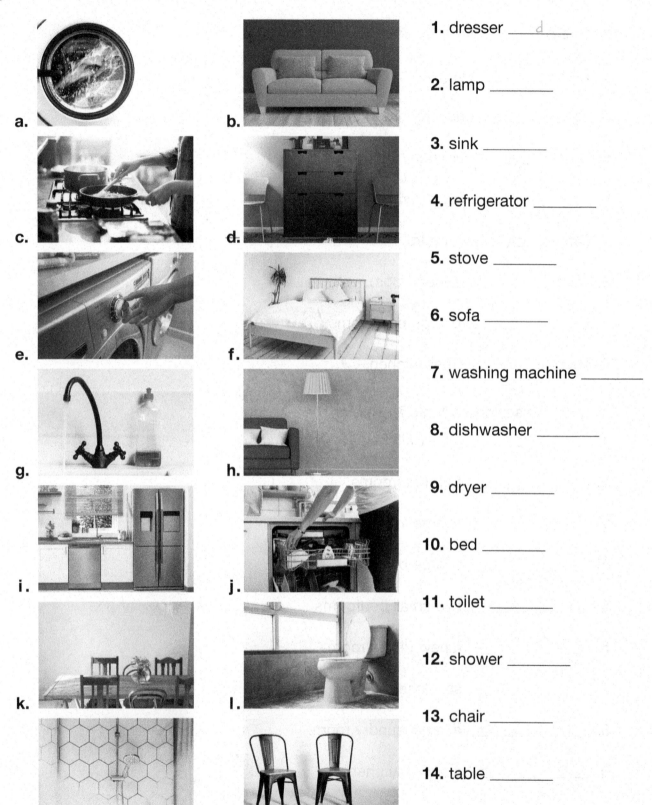

1. dresser ___d___

2. lamp _____

3. sink _____

4. refrigerator _____

5. stove _____

6. sofa _____

7. washing machine _____

8. dishwasher _____

9. dryer _____

10. bed _____

11. toilet _____

12. shower _____

13. chair _____

14. table _____

B Complete the conversations.

1. **A:** _____Is there_____ a sink?

   B: Yes, _____there is_____.

2. **A:** _____ any tables?

   B: No, _____.

3. **A:** _____ any chairs?

   B: No, _____.

4. **A:** _____ a dryer?

   B: No, _____.

5. **A:** _____ any beds?

   B: Yes, _____.

C  Listen to the conversations. Circle *a* or *b*.

1. **a.** There is a stove in the apartment.

   b. There isn't a stove in the apartment

2. **a.** There are lamps in the apartment.

   b. There aren't any lamps in the apartment.

3. **a.** There are chairs in the apartment.

   b. There aren't any chairs in the apartment.

4. **a.** There is a washing machine in the apartment.

   b. There isn't a washing machine in the apartment.

5. **a.** There are tables in the apartment.

   b. There aren't any tables in the apartment.

6. **a.** There is a bed in the apartment.

   b. There isn't a bed in the apartment.

Lesson 4: Give an Address

A Look at the pictures. Complete the addresses.

1. _____14_____ Cherry Lane

2. 1498 _____ Street

3. 5 City _____

4. 910 _____ _____

5. _____ _____ Avenue

6. _____ Lake _____

B ▶ Listen. Complete the addresses.

1. ___13___ Martin Street

2. _____ Angelo Drive

3. _____ Green Boulevard

4. _____ South Lane

5. _____ Meadow Road

6. _____ Erie Avenue

C Read the apartment ads. Circle *a* or *b*.

For rent
1 bedroom
459 Orange Avenue
$675/month

1. What's the address?

   a. 459 Orange Avenue   **b.** $675/month

2. How much is the rent?

   a. 459 Orange Avenue   **b.** $675/month

For rent
3 bedrooms
1326 Cedar Lane
$995/month

3. What's the address?

   a. 1326 Cedar Lane   **b.** $995/month

4. How much is the rent?

   a. 1326 Cedar Lane   **b.** $995/month

For rent
2 bedrooms
15 Ocean Drive
$850/month

5. What's the address?

   a. 15 Ocean Drive   **b.** $850/month

6. How much is the rent?

   a. 15 Ocean Drive   **b.** $850/month

D ▶ Listen to the conversation.

E ▶ Listen to the conversation again. Circle *Yes* or *No*.

1. He is looking for an apartment.   Yes   No

2. The address is 855 Ocean Drive.   Yes   No

3. The rent is $975 a month.   Yes   No

Lesson 5: Life Skills: Address an Envelope

A Match the words with the abbreviations.

1. Street   _d_   **a.** Ln.

2. Drive   ____   **b.** Ave.

3. Boulevard   ____   **c.** Rd.

4. Apartment   ____   ~~d.~~ St.

5. Road   ____   **e.** Blvd.

6. Lane   ____   **f.** Apt.

7. Avenue   ____   **g.** Dr.

B Look at the return address on the envelope. Circle *Yes* or *No*.

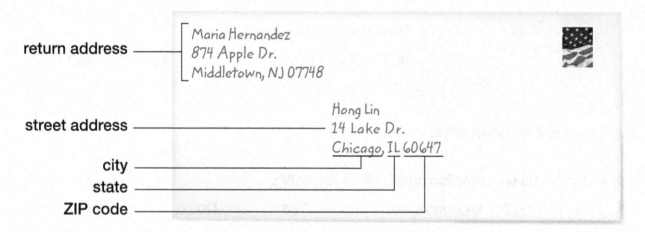

1. The letter is from Maria.   (Yes)   No

2. Maria's last name is Hernandez.   Yes   No

3. The return address is 14 Lake Drive.   Yes   No

4. Ms. Hernandez lives in Middletown.   Yes   No

5. Ms. Hernandez's ZIP code is 60647.   Yes   No

C Look at the envelope again. Where is it going? Circle *Yes* or *No*.

1. The letter is going to Mr. Lin.   (Yes)   No

2. Mr. Lin's first name is Hong.   Yes   No

3. The letter is going to 874 Apple Drive.   Yes   No

4. Mr. Lin lives in Chicago.   Yes   No

5. Mr. Lin's ZIP code is 07748.   Yes   No

D Answer the questions. Use your information.

1. What's your first and last name?   _____

2. What's your address?   _____

3. What's your city and state?   _____

4. What's your ZIP code?   _____

E Think about a friend or a family member. Address an envelope to him or her.

Lesson 6: Read and Write About Moving

A ▶ **Listen to the story. Number the sentences in the correct order.**

___ Pilar has a good job. She works in an office.

_1_ This is Pilar. She is 21 years old. She is single.

___ Pilar wants to live with her friends.

___ Pilar's parents are not happy. In their native country, single people live with their families.

___ Pilar lives with her sister and her sister's husband.

___ In the United States, many single people live with friends.

B **Read the sentences in Exercise A again. Write the sentences in the correct order.**

This is Pilar. She is 21 years old. She is single.
_____

_____

_____

_____

_____

C ▶ **Listen to the story again. Check your answers to Exercise B.**

Lesson 7: English at Work: Talk About Apartments

A Number the sentences in the correct order.

   ___ **Vera:**   There are two bedrooms, a kitchen, and a living room.

   ___ **Customer:** Good morning. I'm looking for a two-bedroom apartment.

   _1_ **Vera:**   Good morning. Can I help you?

   ___ **Vera:**   It's $1,150 a month.

   ___ **Customer:** What's it like?

   ___ **Customer:** What's the address?

   ___ **Customer:** It sounds great! How much is the rent?

   ___ **Vera:**   It's 32 River Street.

   ___ **Vera:**   OK. I have an apartment for rent on River Street.

APARTMENTS!
1 BEDROOM
2 BEDROOM
3 BEDROOM

Vera   Customer

B Read the sentences in Exercise A again. Write the sentences in the correct order.

Vera: _Good morning. Can I help you?_ _____

Customer: _____

Vera: _____

Customer: _____

Vera: _____

Customer: _____

Vera: _____

Customer: _____

Vera: _____

Lesson 1: Identify Clothing You Need

A Look at the pictures. Write the words. Use the words in the box.

a dress	a jacket	jeans	pants	a shirt	shoes
a skirt	~~sneakers~~	socks	a sweater	a T-shirt	

1. _____sneakers_____

2. _____

3. _____

4. _____

5. _____

6. _____

7. _____

8. _____

9. _____

10. _____

11. _____

B ▶ Listen for the clothing. Circle *a*, *b*, or *c*.

1. a.　　　 b.　　　 c.

2. a.　　　 b.　　　 c.

3. a.　　　 b.　　　 c.

4. a.　　　 b.　　　 c.

5. a.　　　 b.　　　 c.

6. a.　　　 b.　　　 c.

C ▶ Listen. Complete the conversations.

1. **A:** Let's go shopping! I need a new ___jacket___.

   B: OK. I need _____shoes_____.

2. **A:** Let's go shopping! I need new _____.

   B: OK. I need _____.

3. **A:** Let's go shopping! I need a new _____.

   B: OK. I need _____.

4. **A:** Let's go shopping! I need new _____.

   B: OK. I need _____.

Lesson 2: Ask for Clothing Sizes

A ▶ **Listen. Complete the conversations.**

1. **A:** Can I help you?

   B: Do you have this shirt in a _____*large*_____?

   A: Yes. Here you go.

   B: Do you have these sneakers in a size _____*11*_____?

   A: I'm sorry. We don't.

2. **A:** Can I help you?

   B: Do you have this dress in a _____?

   A: Yes. Here you go.

   B: Do you have these jeans in a size _____?

   A: I'm sorry. We don't.

3. **A:** Can I help you?

   B: Do you have this T-shirt in an _____?

   A: Yes. Here you go.

   B: Do you have these shoes in a size _____?

   A: I'm sorry. We don't.

B **Complete the sentences. Write *this* or *these*.**

1. Do you have ___*this*___ shirt in a small?

2. We have _____ jacket in an extra large.

3. _____ shirts are medium.

4. _____ dress is a large.

5. Do you have _____ sneakers in a size 10?

C Complete the questions and sentences. Write *that* or *those*.

1. Do you have ____*that*____ skirt in a medium?

2. Do you have _____ pants in a size 2?

3. _____ shirt is a large.

4. _____ sneakers are a size 6.

5. We have _____ jacket in a small.

6. We have _____ jeans in a size 4.

D Look at the pictures. Write *this, that, these,* or *those*.

1. We have ____*those*____ shirts in a large.

2. We have _____ sweater in a small.

3. We have _____ shoes in a size 11.

4. We have _____ dress in a size 10.

Lesson 3: Describe Clothing

A Look at the picture. Write the colors.

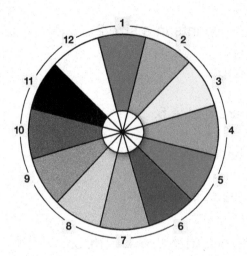

1. _____red_____   5. _____   9. _____

2. _____   6. _____   10. _____

3. _____   7. _____   11. _____

4. _____   8. _____   12. _____

B ▶ Listen for the color. Circle *a* or *b*.

1. **a.** black   **b.** blue

2. **a.** red   **b.** orange

3. **a.** green   **b.** blue

4. **a.** beige   **b.** brown

5. **a.** white   **b.** yellow

6. **a.** pink   **b.** purple

7. **a.** green   **b.** gray

8. **a.** blue   **b.** brown

C Read the story.

Kevin and Sahra are at a department store. The department store has a sale today. Kevin needs a blue sweater and brown shoes. Sahra needs a green sweater and a white skirt. She needs black shoes, too.

D Read the story again. Circle *Yes* or *No*.

1. Kevin and Sahra are at a department store.	Yes	No
2. Kevin needs a brown sweater.	Yes	No
3. Kevin needs black shoes.	Yes	No
4. Sahra needs a green sweater.	Yes	No
5. Sahra needs a blue skirt.	Yes	No
6. Sahra needs black shoes.	Yes	No

E Answer the questions about yourself.

1. What color are your favorite sneakers? _____

2. What color is your favorite sweater? _____

3. What color is your favorite T-shirt? _____

4. What color is your favorite jacket? _____

5. What color are your favorite pants? _____

F Write three things you are wearing. Include the colors.

I am wearing *a red shirt, beige pants, and brown shoes.* _____

I am wearing _____

Lesson 4: Return Clothing to a Store

A Look at the pictures. Write *big*, *long*, *short*, or *small*.

1. It's too _____small_____.

2. They're too _____.

3. It's too _____.

4. They're too _____.

B Look at the pictures. Write sentences. Use *big*, *long*, *short*, or *small*.

1.  _The jacket is too small._____

2.  _____

3.  _____

4.  _____

C Look at the pictures. Complete the conversations. Write the clothes and the problems.

1. **A:** I need to return a _____sweater_____ and

   some _____

   B: What's the problem?

   A: The _____ is too _____,

   and the _____ are too

   _____. Here's my receipt.

2. **A:** I need to return a _____ and

   some _____.

   B: What's the problem?

   A: The _____ is too _____,

   and the _____ are too

   _____. Here's my receipt.

D ▶ Listen to the conversation. Circle *a* or *b*.

1. a. The man needs to buy clothes.

   b. The man needs to return clothes.

2. a. The sweater is too short.

   b. The sweater is too long.

3. a. The sneakers are too small.

   b. The sneakers are too big.

4. a. The man has a receipt.

   b. The man doesn't have a receipt.

Lesson 5: Life Skills: Read Store Ads

A Read the store ad.

CLOTHING MART Sale April 22–29   HOME | WOMEN | MEN | CHILDREN

regular price $40.00
on sale $35.00

regular price $39.00
on sale $25.50

all skirts
on sale

regular price $38.99
on sale $30.00

all sweaters
on sale

regular price $69.99
on sale $59.99

B Read the store ad again. Circle *Yes* or *No*.

1. The sale is at Clothing Mart.	Yes	No
2. The sale is from April 22 – 29.	Yes	No
3. The jeans are on sale for $38.99.	Yes	No
4. The regular price of the shirt is $35.00.	Yes	No
5. You can save $15.00 on dresses.	Yes	No
6. The jacket is on sale for $59.99.	Yes	No
7. The skirts are not on sale.	Yes	No
8. All sweaters are on sale.	Yes	No

C ▶ Listen. Complete the conversations. Use the words in the box.

9:00 $15.50 $19.99 $25.00   ~~Clara's~~   Thursday

1. **A:** What store is having a sale?

   B: _____Clara's_____ Store is having a sale.

2. **A:** When is the sale?

   B: The sale is on _____.

3. **A:** What time does the store open?

   B: The store opens at _____.

4. **A:** How much are the jackets?

   B: The jackets are _____.

5. **A:** How much are the shoes?

   B: The shoes are _____.

6. **A:** How much are the shirts?

   B: The shirts are _____.

D GO ONLINE. Find a sale on a clothing store website. What do you want to buy? Write the clothing items and their prices.

1. I want to buy ____the jeans____. The regular price is ____$42.99____.
   The sale price is ____$35.99____.

2. I want to buy _____. The regular price is _____.
   The sale price is _____.

3. I want to buy _____. The regular price is _____.
   The sale price is _____.

4. I want to buy _____. The regular price is _____.
   The sale price is _____.

Lesson 6: Read and Write About Clothing at a Wedding

A ▶ Listen to the story. Number the sentences in the correct order.

___ In her native country, people wear white clothes at funerals.

_1_ This is Yun. She lives in the United States. She is getting married.

___ Many women wear a red and green dress at their wedding.

___ Yun's mother and grandmother want her to have a red and green dress.

___ Her wedding is in August. She needs a new dress. She wants a white dress.

B Read the sentences in Exercise A again. Write the sentences in the correct order.

This is Yun. She lives in the United States. She is getting married.

_____

_____

_____

_____

C ▶ Listen to the story again. Check your answers to Exercise B.

Lesson 7: English at Work: Help a Customer Return Clothes

A Number the sentences in the correct order.

___ **Omar:** OK. What's the problem?

___ **Customer:** Yes. Here you go.

_1_ **Omar:** Good afternoon. Can I help you?

___ **Omar:** Thank you.

___ **Omar:** Do you have your receipt?

___ **Customer:** I need to return these pants.

___ **Customer:** They are too big.

B Read the sentences in Exercise A again. Write the sentences in the correct order.

Omar: _Good afternoon. Can I help you?_

Customer: _____

Omar: _____

Customer: _____

Omar: _____

Customer: _____

Omar: _____

Unit 9: Our Busy Lives

Lesson 1: Talk About What You Do for Fun

A Match the pictures with the words.

a.

b.

c.

d.

e.

f.

g.

h.

i.

1. exercise _____c_____

2. play video games _____

3. go online _____

4. visit friends _____

5. go to the movies _____

6. listen to music _____

7. play the guitar _____

8. watch TV _____

9. play soccer _____

B Look at Pat's online calendar. Circle *Yes* or *No*.

February

SUNDAY 1	MONDAY 2	TUESDAY 3	WEDNESDAY 4	THURSDAY 5	FRIDAY 6	SATURDAY 7
visit friends	exercise	play soccer play the guitar	exercise	play the guitar	exercise	play soccer
SUNDAY 8	MONDAY 9	TUESDAY 10	WEDNESDAY 11	THURSDAY 12	FRIDAY 13	SATURDAY 14
visit friends	exercise	play soccer play the guitar	exercise	play the guitar	exercise	play soccer
SUNDAY 15	MONDAY 16	TUESDAY 17	WEDNESDAY 18	THURSDAY 19	FRIDAY 20	SATURDAY 21
visit friends	exercise	play soccer play the guitar	exercise	play the guitar	exercise	play soccer
SUNDAY 22	MONDAY 23	TUESDAY 24	WEDNESDAY 25	THURSDAY 26	FRIDAY 27	SATURDAY 28
visit friends	exercise	play soccer play the guitar	exercise	play the guitar	exercise	play soccer

1. Pat visits friends once a week.   (Yes)   No

2. Pat exercises three times a week.   Yes   No

3. Pat plays soccer three times a week.   Yes   No

4. Pat plays the guitar every Tuesday and Thursday.   Yes   No

5. Pat plays soccer every Monday and Friday.   Yes   No

6. Pat goes to the movies every Saturday.   Yes   No

7. Pat goes to English class every Thursday.   Yes   No

C Answer the questions about yourself.

1. What do you do in your free time?

_____

2. How often?

_____

Lesson 2: Talk About What You Are Doing

A Complete the conversations. Use the words in parentheses.

1. **A:** Hello?

   B: Hi Marco. Are you busy?

   A: I'm (play / the guitar) ___playing the guitar___.
   Can I call you later?

   B: No problem. Bye.

   A: Goodbye.

2. **A:** Hello?

   B: Hi Maria. Are you busy?

   A: I'm (go / to the library) _____.
   Can I call you later?

   B: No problem. Bye.

   A: Goodbye.

3. **A:** Hello?

   B: Hi Alex. Are you busy?

   A: I'm (play / video games) _____.
   Can I call you later?

   B: No problem. Bye.

   A: Goodbye.

4. **A:** Hello?

   B: Hi Elsa. Are you busy?

   A: I'm (go / to the movies) _____.
   Can I call you later?

   B: No problem. Bye.

   A: Goodbye.

B Read the sentences. Rewrite them with contractions.

1. She is going online.   *She's going online.*

2. You are playing video games. _____

3. They are watching TV. _____

4. We are listening to music. _____

5. He is going to the movies. _____

6. I am playing soccer. _____

7. She is exercising. _____

8. You are visiting friends. _____

9. I am playing the guitar. _____

C Write sentences. Use the correct form of the verbs. Use contractions.

1. (He / play soccer) *He's playing soccer.*

2. (We / go to the movies) _____

3. (I / go online) _____

4. (She / exercise) _____

5. (They / listen to music) _____

6. (You / watch TV) _____

7. (We / play the guitar) _____

8. (I / visit friends) _____

9. (He / play video games) _____

Lesson 3: Ask About Ongoing Activities

A Look at the pictures. Write the household chores. Use the words in the box.

do homework   feed the cat   pay bills

~~talk on the phone~~   walk the dog   wash the car

1. ___talk on the phone___   2. _____   3. _____

4. _____   5. _____   6. _____

B Read the conversations. Complete the answers.

1. A: Is he washing the car?   **B:** Yes, _____he is_____.

2. A: Is she walking the dog?   **B:** No, _____.

3. A: Is she talking on the phone?   **B:** Yes, _____.

4. A: Are the students doing homework?   **B:** Yes, _____.

5. A: Is he feeding the cat?   **B:** No, _____.

6. A: Are they paying bills?   **B:** Yes, _____.

C Write the questions.

1. (you / wash the car) _Are you washing the car?_

2. (Evan / pay bills) _____

3. (Cara and Tom / study English) _____

4. (Julie / visit friends) _____

5. (he / play soccer) _____

6. (we / do homework) _____

D ▶ Listen to the conversation.

E ▶ Listen to the conversation again. Circle *Yes* or *No*.

1. Ming is talking on the phone.   (Yes)   No

2. Jack is doing his homework.   Yes   No

3. Jack is not studying English.   Yes   No

4. Mary is not doing her homework.   Yes   No

5. Mary is watching TV.   Yes   No

F Answer the questions about yourself.

1. Are you doing homework?   _____

2. Are you talking on the phone?   _____

3. Are you studying English?   _____

4. Are you writing?   _____

Lesson 4: Talk About Ongoing Activities at Work

A Look at the pictures. Write the workplace activities. Use the words in the box.

answer the phone   count money   drive a truck

fix cars   help a customer   look for something

take a break   take orders   ~~work on the computer~~

1. *work on the computer*

2. _____

3. _____

4. _____

5. _____

6. _____

7. _____

8. _____

9. _____

B Complete the conversations. Write *he's*, *she's*, *I'm* or *they're* and *not*.

1. A: Is he working on the computer?

   B: No, _*he's not*_ working on the computer. He's helping a customer.

2. A: Are they fixing cars?

   B: No, _____ fixing cars. They're counting money.

3. A: Are you taking a break?

   B: No, _____ taking a break. I'm taking orders.

4. A: Is she driving a truck?

   B: No, _____ driving a truck. She's looking for something.

5. A: Is he helping a customer?

   B: No, _____ helping a customer. He's taking a break.

C Look at the pictures. Write sentences. Use contractions.

1. _She's not driving a truck._

2. _____

3. _____

4. _____

Lesson 5: Life Skills: Leave a Voicemail

A Read the voicemail. Complete the sentences.

1. The voicemail is for _____ Dan Green _____.

2. The date is _____.

3. The time is _____.

4. The caller is _____.

5. Her phone number is _____.

6. Her message is that she can't come to work because _____

_____.

Hana Brown
2/19/18 at 4:04 P.M.

▶ ●━━━━━━━━━━━━━━━━━━━

This is Dan Green. Please leave a message.

Transcript
"Hi, Dan! This is Hana Brown. I can't come to work because I'm sick. Sorry! My number is 718-555-2342."

Alan Smith
8/13/19 at 9:32 P.M.

▶ ●━━━━━━━━━━━━━━━━━━━

This is Sofia Garcia. Please leave a message.

Transcript
"Hi, Sofia! This is Alan Smith. I will be late to school because I missed the bus."

7. The voicemail is for _____ Sofia Garcia _____.

8. The date is _____.

9. The time is _____.

10. The caller is _____.

11. His message is that he will be late to school because _____

_____.

B ▶ Listen. Complete the information from the phone calls.

1.

MESSAGE

For: _Mr. Clark_   Date: _9/23/18_

Caller: _____   Phone: _____

Message: _____

_____

_____

2.

MESSAGE

For: _____   Date: _4/5/19_

Caller: _____   Phone: _____

Message: _____

_____

_____

3.

MESSAGE

For: _____   Date: _6/16/19_

Caller: _____   Phone: _____

Message: _____

_____

_____

Lesson 6: Read and Write About Weekend Schedules

A ▶ **Listen to the story. Number the sentences in the correct order.**

___ Luis and his wife eat alone on weekends.

_1_ This is Luis. He lives in the United States. He has two children.

___ They spend time together. They talk.

___ His children are busy on weekends. They talk to their friends. They play sports.

___ In Luis's native country, families are together on weekends.

___ Their children are busy every Saturday and Sunday.

B **Read the sentences in Exercise A again. Write the sentences in the correct order.**

This is Luis. He lives in the United States. He has two children.

_____

_____

_____

_____

_____

C ▶ **Listen to the story again. Check your answers to Exercise B.**

Lesson 7: English at Work: Take a Personal Call

A Number the sentences in the correct order.

___ **Ken:** Oh! Sorry to bother you. Are you working tonight?

_1_ **Ken:** Hi, Pam. It's Ken. What are you doing?

___ **Pam:** No, I'm not. I'm going home at 5:00. I can call you then.

___ **Pam:** I'm working right now. Can I call you later?

___ **Ken:** OK, great. Bye!

B Read the sentences in Exercise A again. Write the sentences in the correct order.

Ken: _Hi, Pam. It's Ken. What are you doing?_ _____

Pam: _____

Ken: _____

Pam: _____

Ken: _____

Unit 10: Where's the Bus Stop?

Lesson 1: Ask About Places in the Community

A Match the pictures with the words.

a.

b.

c.

d.

e.

f.

g.

h.

i.

1. a supermarket ____f____

2. a drugstore _____

3. a restaurant _____

4. a hospital _____

5. a bus stop _____

6. a bank _____

7. an ATM _____

8. a parking lot _____

9. a convenience store _____

B Look at the map. Complete the conversations.

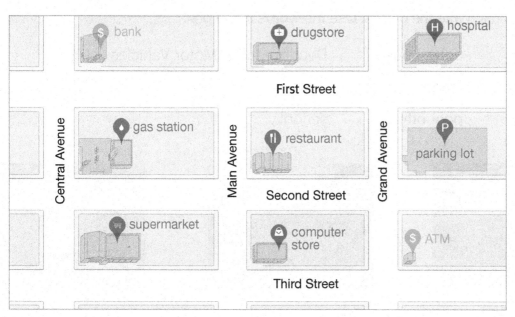

1. **A:** Excuse me. Is there a parking lot near here?

   B: Yes. There's _____*a parking lot*_____ on the corner of _____*Grand Avenue*_____ and
   _____*Second Street*_____.

   A: Thank you!

2. **A:** Excuse me. Is there a restaurant near here?

   B: Yes. There's _____ on the corner of _____ and
   _____.

   A: Thank you!

3. **A:** Excuse me. Where is the gas station?

   B: There's _____ on the corner of _____ and
   _____.

   A: Thanks.

4. **A:** Excuse me. Is there a supermarket near here?

   B: Yes. There's _____ on the corner of _____ and
   _____.

   A: Thanks!

Lesson 2: Ask Where Places Are

A Look at the pictures. Write the places. Use the words in the box.

City Hall   court house   Department of Motor Vehicles (DMV)

fire station   library   park

police station   ~~post office~~   school

1. _____*post office*_____

2. _____

3. _____

4. _____

5. _____

6. _____

7. _____

8. _____

9. _____

B Look at the map. Write *across from* or *between*.

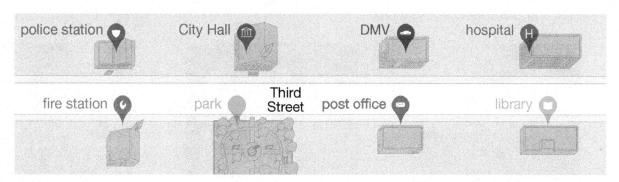

1. **A:** Where's the park?

   B: It's _____across from_____ City Hall.

2. **A:** Where's the library?

   B: It's _____ the hospital.

3. **A:** Where's City Hall?

   B: It's _____ the police station and the DMV.

4. **A:** Where's the fire station?

   B: It's _____ the police station.

5. **A:** Where's the DMV?

   B: It's _____ City Hall and the hospital.

6. **A:** Where's the police station?

   B: It's _____ the fire station.

7. **A:** Where's the post office?

   B: It's _____ the park and the library.

8. **A:** Where's the hospital?

   B: It's _____ the library.

Lesson 3: Ask About Transportation

A Match the pictures with the words.

a.

b.

c.

d.

e.

f.

g.

h.

i.

1. walk ___g___

2. take the subway _____

3. ride a bike _____

4. take a taxi _____

5. drive _____

6. take the bus _____

7. carpool _____

8. take the train _____

9. take a ferry _____

B ▶ Listen. Complete the conversations. Use the words in the box.

drive   take a taxi   ~~take the bus~~   take the train

1. **A:** Where are you going?

   B: I'm going to English class.

   A: How do you get to school?

   B: I _____take the bus_____.

2. **A:** Where are you going?

   B: I'm going to work.

   A: How do you get to work?

   B: I _____.

3. **A:** Where are you going?

   B: I'm going to the library.

   A: How do you get to the library?

   B: I _____.

4. **A:** Where are you going?

   B: I'm going to the supermarket.

   A: How do you get to the supermarket?

   B: I _____.

C Answer the questions about yourself.

1. How do you get to school?   _____

2. How do you get to work?   _____

3. How do you get to the library?   _____

4. How do you get to the supermarket?   _____

Lesson 4: Ask for and Give Directions

A Look at the arrows. Write the directions. Use the words in the box.

Go straight.   Turn left.   Turn right.   Go two blocks.

1. _____

2. _____

3. _____

4. _____

B ▶ Listen. Complete the conversations.

1. **A:** Excuse me. Where's the train station?

    B: It's on First Avenue. _____*Go*_____ ___*straight*___ for one block.

    Then _____ _____ on First Avenue.

    A: Thanks a lot!

2. **A:** Excuse me. Where's the supermarket?

    B: It's on Second Avenue. _____ _____ on Main Street.

    Then _____ _____ for one block.

    A: Thanks a lot!

3. **A:** Excuse me. Where's the bank?

    B: It's on Third Avenue. _____ _____ on Central Street.

    Then _____ _____ on Third Avenue.

    A: Thanks a lot!

C Look at the maps. Read the directions. Write the places.

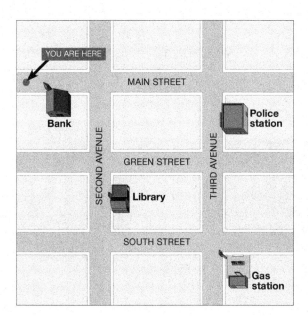

1. Go straight for two blocks.

Then turn right on Third Avenue.

police station

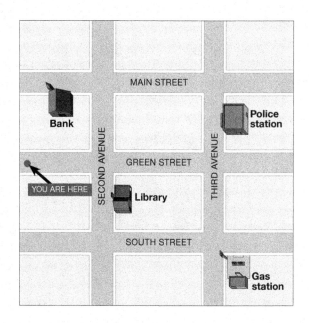

2. Go straight for one block.

Then turn right on Second Avenue.

_____

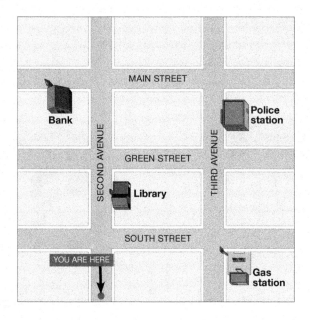

3. Go straight for three blocks.

Then turn left on Main Street.

_____

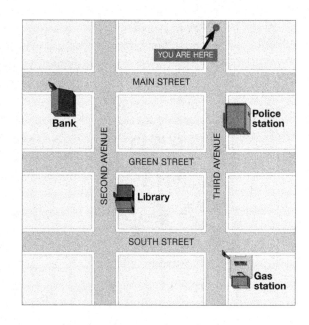

4. Go straight for three blocks.

Then turn left on South Street.

_____

Lesson 5: Life Skills: Read Traffic Signs

A Look at the pictures. Write the words. Use the words in the box.

don't walk   no left turn   ~~no parking~~   no U-turn   one-way street

speed limit   stop   crosswalk   do not enter

1. _____no parking_____

2. _____

3. _____

4. _____

5. _____

6. _____

7. _____

8. _____

9. _____

B Look at the picture. Circle *Yes* or *No*.

1. Do you stop?   Yes   No

2. Do you walk?   Yes   No

3. Do you stop?   Yes   No

4. Do you park here?   Yes   No

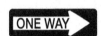

5. Do you go one-way only?   Yes   No

6. Do you turn left?   Yes   No

7. Do you enter?   Yes   No

8. Do you make a U-turn?   Yes   No

Lesson 6: Read and Write About Transportation

A ▶ **Listen to the story. Number the sentences in the correct order.**

___ In Mohammed's native country, he takes the bus to get to work.

___ Mohammed lives in the United States. He has a car.

_1_ This is Mohammed.

___ In the United States, Mohammed drives to work.

___ He drives to English class. He drives to go shopping.

___ He takes the subway to get to English class.

___ He takes a taxi to go shopping.

B **Read the sentences in Exercise A again. Write the story.**

This is Mohammed.

_____

_____

_____

_____

_____

_____

_____

C ▶ **Listen to the story again. Check your answers to Exercise B.**

Lesson 7: English at Work: Give Directions

A Number the sentences in the correct order.

___ **Ali:** Go two blocks to the left. It's across from the fire station.

_1_ **Customer:** Excuse me. Where is the library?

___ **Customer:** Go two blocks and turn left. I understand. Thank you!

___ **Ali:** You're welcome!

___ **Ali:** No problem. Go two blocks and turn left on Park Street.

___ **Customer:** I'm sorry. Can you repeat that?

B Read the sentences in Exercise A again. Write the sentences in the correct order.

Customer: _Excuse me. Where is the library?_____

Ali: _____

Customer: _____

Ali: _____

Customer: _____

Ali: _____

Lesson 1: Make an Appointment

A Look at the pictures. Write the parts of the body. Use the words in the box.

arm	chest	ear	eye	stomach	hand	~~head~~	knee
leg	mouth	neck	nose	shoulder	foot / feet	back	

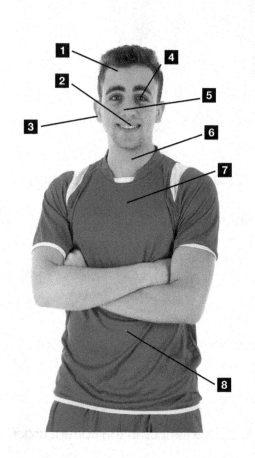
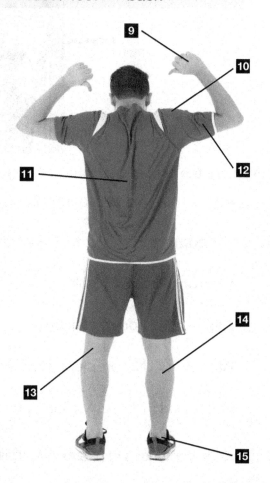

1. _____head_____   6. _____   11. _____

2. _____   7. _____   12. _____

3. _____   8. _____   13. _____

4. _____   9. _____   14. _____

5. _____   10. _____   15. _____

B ► Listen for the part of the body. Circle *a* or *b*.

1. **a.** stomach   **b.** shoulder

2. **a.** hand   **b.** arm

3. **a.** foot   **b.** feet

4. **a.** ear   **b.** eye

5. **a.** feet   **b.** knee

6. **a.** chest   **b.** leg

7. **a.** neck   **b.** nose

8. **a.** hand   **b.** arm

C Look at the pictures. Complete the sentences.

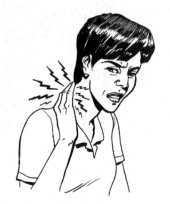

1. Her ____*neck hurts*____.

2. His _____.

3. Her _____.

4. His _____.

Lesson 2: Listen to a Doctor

A Look at the pictures. Complete the sentences. Use the words in the box.

Breathe   jacket   mouth   out   Lie

sleeves   Step   straight   table

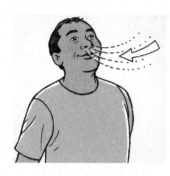

1. _Breathe_ in.

2. Roll up your _____.

3. Look _____ ahead.

4. _____ down.

5. Take off your _____.

6. Open your _____.

7. Breathe _____.

8. _____ on the scale.

9. Sit on the _____.

B ▶ Listen to the instructions. Match the instructions with the pictures.

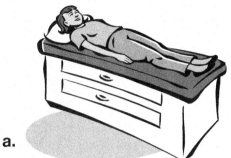

a.

b.

c.

d.

1. __b__   **2.** _____   **3.** _____   **4.** _____

C Read the story.

Joe gets a checkup every year. He has an appointment on Thursday. He goes to the health clinic. The doctor checks him. Joe follows the doctor's instructions. The doctor says, "You are in good health."

D Read the story again. Circle *Yes* or *No*.

1. Joe gets a checkup every year.	Yes	No
2. Joe has a doctor's appointment on Tuesday.	Yes	No
3. His appointment is at the health clinic.	Yes	No
4. Joe gives the doctor instructions.	Yes	No
5. Joe is in good health.	Yes	No

Lesson 3: Offer Suggestions

A Match the pictures with the words.

a.

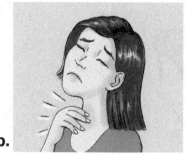
b.

c.

d.

e.

f.

g.

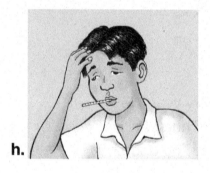
h.

i.

1. the flu ___e___

2. a stomachache _____

3. a cough _____

4. a fever _____

5. a headache _____

6. a sore throat _____

7. a backache _____

8. a cold _____

9. a toothache _____

B Look at the pictures. Write the correct suggestions from the box.

drink a lot of liquids   get a lot of rest   stay home from work   ~~take aspirin~~

1. **A:** What's the matter?

   B: I have a headache.

   A: You should _____ *take aspirin* _____.

2. **A:** What's the matter?

   B: I have a cold.

   A: You should _____.

3. **A:** What's the matter?

   B: I have a fever.

   A: You should _____.

4. **A:** What's the matter?

   B: I have the flu.

   A: You should _____.

C Write suggestions. Use *should*.

1. (take aspirin) _____ *You should take aspirin.* _____

2. (get a lot of rest) _____

3. (stay home from school) _____

4. (drink a lot of liquids) _____

Lesson 4: Call 911 for Emergencies

A Describe the emergencies. Use the sentences in the box.

My friend is having a heart attack.

~~Someone robbed my house.~~

There is a building on fire.

There was a car accident.

1. ____Someone robbed my house.____

2. _____

3. _____

4. _____

B ▶ Listen to the conversation. Choose the correct sentences. Circle *a* or *b*.

1. **a.** Someone robbed the woman's house.

   b. The woman is having a heart attack.

2. **a.** The woman is on Main Street.

   b. The woman is on Oak Street.

3. **a.** The woman is in Oak City.

   b. The woman is in Lake City.

4. **a.** The cross street is Main Street.

   b. The cross street is Oak Street.

C ▶ **Listen to the conversations. Write the missing words and numbers.**

1. **A:** 911. What's your emergency?

   B: There is a building on _____*fire*_____.

   A: Where are you?

   B: _____*1402*_____ Oak Avenue in Park City.

   A: What's the cross street?

   B: Third Street.

2. **A:** 911. What's your emergency?

   B: My friend is having a _____ attack.

   A: Where are you?

   B: _____ Park Avenue in River City.

   A: What's the cross street?

   B: First Street.

3. **A:** 911. What's your emergency?

   B: Someone _____ my house.

   A: Where are you?

   B: _____ Third Avenue in Maple City.

   A: What's the cross street?

   B: Main Street.

4. **A:** 911. What's your emergency?

   B: There was a _____ accident.

   A: Where are you?

   B: _____ Fourth Avenue in Green City.

   A: What's the cross street?

   B: Lake Street.

Lesson 5: Life Skills: Read a Medicine Label

A Look at the pictures. Circle *a* or *b*.

1. **a.** cough syrup
   b. aspirin

2. **a.** one teaspoon
   b. two teaspoons

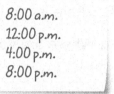

8:00 a.m.
12:00 p.m.
4:00 p.m.
8:00 p.m.

3. **a.** every four hours
   b. twice a day

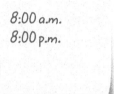

4. **a.** capsules
   b. tablets

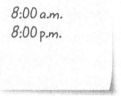

8:00 a.m.
8:00 p.m.

5. **a.** every four hours
   b. twice a day

6. **a.** cough syrup
   b. prescription medicine

8:00 a.m.
2:00 p.m.
8:00 p.m.

7. **a.** every six hours
   b. every four hours

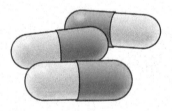

8. **a.** tablets
   b. capsules

9. **a.** prescription medicine
   b. cough syrup

B ▶ Listen to the conversation. Circle *Yes* or *No*.

1. Miguel doesn't feel well.	Yes	No
2. He has a fever and a headache.	Yes	No
3. He is taking prescription medicine.	Yes	No
4. The directions say take two tablets twice a day.	Yes	No
5. The directions say take the medicine with food.	Yes	No

C Read the directions on the medicine label.

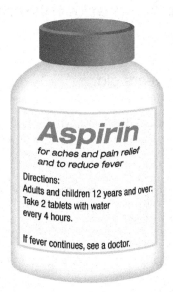

Aspirin
for aches and pain relief
and to reduce fever

Directions:
Adults and children 12 years and over:
Take 2 tablets with water
every 4 hours.

If fever continues, see a doctor.

D Read the directions on the label again. Complete the sentences. Use the words in the box.

two tablets   four hours   aspirin   doctor   ~~pain and fever~~   water

1. The medicine is for ___pain and fever___.

2. Sara has a headache and a fever. She should take some _____.

3. Sara is 32 years old. She should take _____.

4. Sara should take the medicine every _____.

5. Sara should take the medicine with _____.

6. After six days, Sara still has a fever. She should see a _____.

Lesson 6: Read and Write About a Doctor's Appointment

A ▶ Listen to the story. Number the sentences in the correct order.

___ Teresa lives in the United States.

_1_ This is Teresa. She is 45 years old.

___ Her daughter says people should go to the doctor every year.

___ In Teresa's native country, people go to the doctor when they are sick.

___ Her daughter wants her to get a checkup.

___ Teresa feels healthy. She does not want to get a checkup.

B Read the sentences in Exercise A again. Write the story.

This is Teresa.

_____

_____

_____

_____

_____

_____

C ▶ Listen to the story again. Check your answers to Exercise B.

Lesson 7: English at Work: Help Someone Make an Appointment

A Number the sentences in the correct order.

___ **Lila:** Of course! Can you come in at 3:00?

___ **Patient:** Hello. I'd like to make an appointment.

___ **Lila:** See you then!

___ **Patient:** My neck hurts. I want to see a doctor.

___ **Lila:** OK. How about 4:00?

_1_ **Lila:** Thank you for calling Sunshine Clinic. How can I help you?

___ **Patient:** Perfect. Thank you.

___ **Patient:** No, I can't. I can come in after 3:30.

___ **Lila:** OK. What's the problem?

B Read the sentences in Exercise A again. Write the sentences in the correct order.

Lila: _Thank you for calling Sunshine Clinic. How can I help you?_

Patient: _____

Lila: _____

Patient: _____

Lila: _____

Patient: _____

Lila: _____

Patient: _____

Lila: _____

Unit 12: What Do You Do?

Lesson 1: Say Your Occupation

A Match the pictures with the words.

 a.

 b.

 c.

 d.

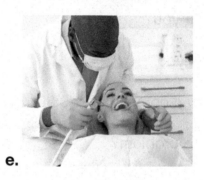 e.

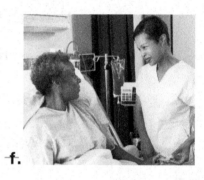 f.

 g.

 h.

 i.

1. a nursing assistant _____ f

2. a teacher's assistant _____

3. a housekeeper _____

4. a painter _____

5. a bus driver _____

6. a sales assistant _____

7. a mechanic _____

8. a dentist _____

9. a construction worker _____

B Look at the pictures. Write the jobs. Use the words in the box.

a sales assistant   a construction worker   a dentist   a bus driver

a housekeeper   a nursing assistant   a̶ ̶m̶e̶c̶h̶a̶n̶i̶c̶   a painter

1. A: What do you do?

    B: I'm _____ a mechanic _____.

2. A: What do you do?

    B: I'm _____.

3. A: What do you do?

    B: I'm _____.

4. A: What do you do?

    B: I'm _____.

5. A: What do you do?

    B: I'm _____.

6. A: What do you do?

    B: I'm _____.

7. A: What do you do?

    B: I'm _____.

8. A: What do you do?

    B: I'm _____.

Lesson 2: Ask About Someone's Job

A Look at the pictures. Write the jobs. Use the words in the box.

a security guard   a cook   ~~a custodian~~   a doctor   a server

a factory worker   a nurse   an office assistant   a cashier

1. _____a custodian_____

2. _____

3. _____

4. _____

5. _____

6. _____

7. _____

8. _____

9. _____

B Complete the questions. Write *do* or *does*.

1. Where _____*does*_____ he work?

2. Where _____ they work?

3. Where _____ Maria work?

4. Where _____ she work?

5. Where _____ you work?

6. Where _____ Sun-Li and Ann work?

7. Where _____ Tom work?

8. Where _____ Bill and Chad work?

C Write questions. Use the words in parentheses and *Where do* or *Where does*.

1. (you / work) _____*Where do you work?*_____

2. (Nancy / work) _____

3. (they / work) _____

4. (Rafal / work) _____

5. (Tien and Monika / work) _____

6. (she / work) _____

D Answer the questions about yourself.

1. Where do you work? _____

2. Where does your teacher work? _____

3. Where does your doctor work? _____

4. Where does your friend work? _____

Lesson 3: Talk About Job Skills

A Look at the pictures. Write the job skills. Use the words in the box.

build houses	operate machinery	take care of patients
help customers	speak two languages	use a cash register
use a computer	use office machines	fix something

1. _____fix something_____

2. _____

3. _____

4. _____

5. _____

6. _____

7. _____

8. _____

9. _____

B Complete the conversations. Use the words in the box.

use office machines	fix cars	~~help customers~~
take care of patients	build houses	use a cash register

1. **A:** What are your job skills?

   B: I'm a sales assistant.

   I can _____ help customers _____.

   And I can use a cash register.

2. **A:** What are your job skills?

   B: I'm a construction worker.

   I can _____.

   And I can speak two languages.

3. **A:** What are your job skills?

   B: I'm a mechanic. I can _____.

   And I can help customers.

4. **A:** What are your job skills?

   B: I'm a doctor. I can _____.

   And I can speak three languages.

5. **A:** What are your job skills?

   B: I'm a cashier. I can _____.

   And I can help customers.

6. **A:** What are your job skills?

   B: I'm an office assistant. I can _____.

   And I can use a computer.

Lesson 4: Apply for a Job

A Complete the answers. Use *I, he, she,* or *they* and *can* or *can't*.

1. **A:** Can you fix cars?   **B:** Yes, _____ I can _____.

2. **A:** Can he use a computer?   **B:** No, _____.

3. **A:** Can she help customers?   **B:** No, _____.

4. **A:** Can they speak two languages?   **B:** Yes, _____.

5. **A:** Can he drive a truck?   **B:** Yes, _____.

B Look at the pictures. Complete the questions. Answer the questions about yourself.

1. **A:** Can you _____ use a computer _____?

     B: _____.

2. **A:** Can you _____?

     B: _____.

3. **A:** Can you _____?

     B: _____.

4. **A:** Can you _____?

     B: _____.

C Put the words in the correct order. Write questions and answers.

1. (Mrs. Smith / can / speak two languages)

   A: _____Can Mrs. Smith speak two languages_____?

   B: Yes, _____she can_____.

2. (use a computer / can / Mr. Lim)

   A: _____?

   B: No, _____.

3. (fix cars / can / Ms. Popova)

   A: _____?

   B: Yes, _____.

4. (you / build houses / can)

   A: _____?

   B: No, _____.

5. (use a cash register / can / Eric and Katrina)

   A: _____?

   B: Yes, _____.

6. (help customers / can / you)

   A: _____?

   B: No, _____.

7. (use office machines / can / Mr. Nowak)

   A: _____?

   B: Yes, _____.

8. (drive a truck / can / Alex and Marie)

   A: _____?

   B: No, _____.

Lesson 5: Life Skills: Read a Job Ad

A Read the job ad.

> **Help Wanted**
> Nursing Assistant
> 2 years of experience required
> Must work well under pressure
> Full-time evenings and
>   weekends
> Apply online: Healthfirst.com

B Read the job ad again. Circle *Yes* or *No*.

1. The job is full-time.	(Yes)	No
2. The job is for a mechanic.	Yes	No
3. Experience is required.	Yes	No
4. You need to work Saturday and Sunday.	Yes	No
5. You need to apply in person.	Yes	No

C Read the job ads.

A.
> **Help Wanted**
> Factory Worker
> Exp req
> PT
> weekends
> Apply in person

B.
> **Help Wanted**
> Supermarket Cashier position
> FT M-F
> call 718-555-9216 for
> an interview appointment

D Read the ads in Exercise C again. Match the sentences with the ads. Circle *A* or *B*.

1. The job is for a factory worker.   (A)   B

2. The job is full-time.   A   B

3. The job is part-time.   A   B

4. You need experience.   A   B

5. You need to work on weekends.   A   B

6. You need to work Monday to Friday.   A   B

7. You need to call for an interview.   A   B

8. You need to apply in person.   A   B

E Match the sentences.

1. I work 12 hours a week.   __d__   a. I work full-time.

2. I need to have experience.   _____   b. I have to go in person.

3. I was a housekeeper in my native country.   _____   c. I work weekends.

4. I have to go to the office for an interview.   _____   d. I work part-time.

5. I work 40 hours a week.   _____   e. Experience is required.

6. I work Saturdays and Sundays.   _____   f. I have experience as a housekeeper.

F Read the sentences. Circle *Yes* or *No* about yourself.

1. I work full-time.	Yes	No
2. I work part-time.	Yes	No
3. I have experience as a cook.	Yes	No
4. I have experience as a housekeeper.	Yes	No
5. I work weekends.	Yes	No
6. I work Monday to Friday.	Yes	No

Lesson 6: Read and Write About a Job Interview

A ▶ **Listen to the story. Number the sentences in the correct order.**

___ Monika is ready for the interview.

___ She practiced her interview skills in her English class.

_1_ This is Monika. She lives in the United States.

___ Monika has a job interview on Thursday at 9:00.

___ Monika gets to the interview. She is early.

___ She says hello and smiles.

___ Mr. Cruz asks about Monika's job skills. She answers his questions.

___ She shakes hands with Mr. Cruz.

B **Read the sentences in Exercise A again. Write the story.**

This is Monika.

_____

_____

_____

_____

_____

_____

_____

_____

C ▶ **Listen to the story again. Check your answers to Exercise B.**

Lesson 7: English at Work: Apply for a New Job

A Number the sentences in the correct order.

___ **Van:** Thank you! I can do it now.

___ **Manager:** OK. Please fill out an application.

___ **Van:** I can start next week!

___ **Manager:** OK. Do you have experience?

___ **Van:** Yes, I do. I work at Tom's Cars now. I have five years of experience.

___ **Manager:** That's great! When can you begin work?

_1_ **Van:** Hello. I'd like to apply for the job.

B Read the sentences in Exercise A again. Write the sentences in the correct order.

Van: _Hello. I'd like to apply for the job._

Manager: _____

Van: _____

Manager: _____

Van: _____

Manager: _____

Van: _____

Writing Practice

A A

B B

C C

D D

E E

F F

G G

H H

I I

J J

K K

L L

M M

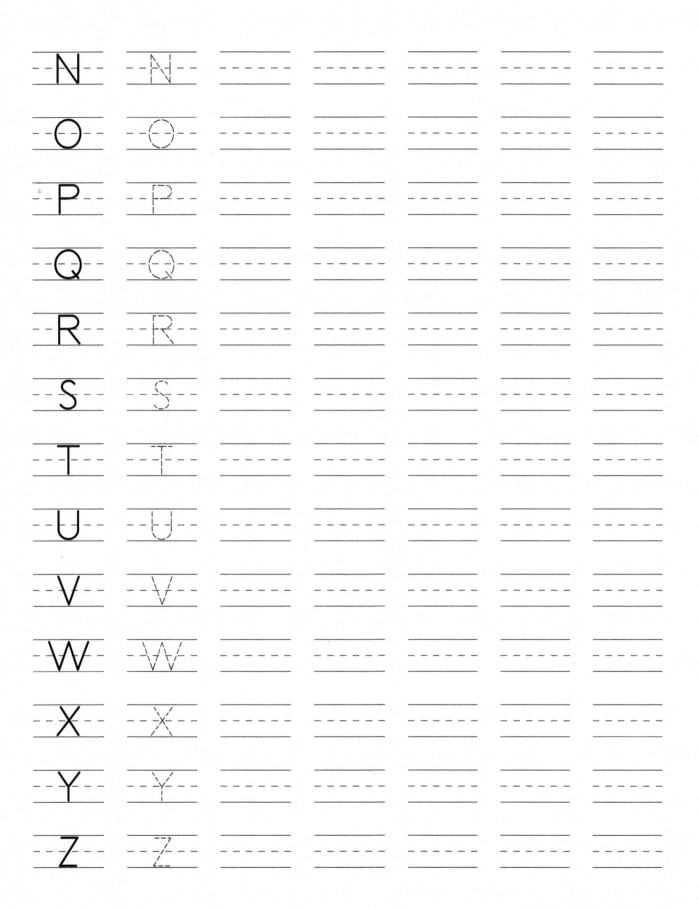

a   a

b   b

c   c

d   d

e   e

f   f

g   g

h   h

i   i

j   j

k   k

l   l

m   m

n n

o o

p p

q q

r r

s s

t t

u u

v v

w w

x x

y y

z z

Audio Script

UNIT 1

UNIT 1
Page 4, Exercise C
1. A: What's your name, please?
   B: My name is Hong Chen.
   A: Spell your first name.
   B: H-O-N-G.
   A: Spell your last name.
   B: C-H-E-N.
2. A: What's your name, please?
   B: My name is Anna Novak.
   A: Spell your first name.
   B: A-N-N-A.
   A: Spell your last name.
   B: N-O-V-A-K.
3. A: What's your name, please?
   B: My name is Mark Smith.
   A: Spell your first name.
   B: M-A-R-K.
   A: Spell your last name.
   B: S-M-I-T-H.
4. A: What's your name, please?
   B: My name is Carla Diaz.
   A: Spell your first name.
   B: C-A-R-L-A.
   A: Spell your last name.
   B: D-I-A-Z.

Page 5, Exercise B
1. A: What's your student ID number?
   B: 53691.
   A: 53691?
   B: That's right.
2. A: What's your student ID number?
   B: 02469.
   A: 02469?
   B: That's right.
3. A: What's your student ID number?
   B: 26750.
   A: 26750?
   B: That's right.
4. A: What's your student ID number?
   B: 63980.
   A: 63980?
   B: That's right.

Page 5, Exercise C
1. A: What's your phone number?
   B: 674-555-5831.
2. A: What's your phone number?
   B: 829-555-1194.
3. A: What's your phone number?
   B: 674-555-5831.

4. A: What's your phone number?
   B: 829-555-1194.
5. A: What's your phone number?
   B: 914-555-8132.
6. A: What's your phone number?
   B: 201-555-4990.

Page 8, Exercise C
1. She's the teacher.
2. He's from Canada.
3. She's my friend.
4. She's a good teacher.
5. He's a new student.
6. She's from El Salvador.
7. He's a good student.
8. He's from Korea.

Page 10, Exercise B
1. They're from Somalia.
2. We're from the United States.
3. They're in the classroom.
4. You're a good student.
5. We're new students.
6. You're my classmate.

Page 12, Exercise A and C
This is Ivan. He is a student.
He says hello to his classmates and smiles.
In his school, some students say hello and shake hands.
Some students say hello and hug.
Some students say hello and bow.
Other students say hello and kiss.

UNIT 2
Page 15, Exercise B
1. Do you have a notebook?
2. Do you have a backpack?
3. Do you have a pen?
4. Do you have a phone?
5. Do you have a dictionary app?

Page 19, Exercise B
1. A: Where is Mr. Lee?
   B: He's in the library.
2. A: Where is Carol?
   B: She's in the cafeteria.
3. A: Where is your teacher?
   B: He's in the classroom.
4. A: Where is your classmate?
   B: She's in the bookstore.
5. A: Where is your book?
   B: It's in the computer lab.

6. A: Where is Yolanda?
   B: She's in the office.

Page 23, Exercise B

A: How do you study English?
B: I go to class, and I ask the teacher questions.
A: That's great!
B: How do you study English?
A: I practice with my classmates. At home, I write in my notebook.

Page 24, Exercise A and C

This is Lan.
In her native country, students do not talk in class.
They listen to the teacher.
In the United States, students talk in groups.
Students ask questions.
The teacher listens to the students.

UNIT 3
Page 26, Exercise A

1. 9   2. 15
3. 23   4. 36
5. 40   6. 52

Page 28, Exercise B

1. A: What time is your English class?
   B: It's at 9:15.
2. A: What time is your break?
   B: It's at 10:40.
3. A: What time is your computer class?
   B: It's at 12:30.
4. A: What time is your break?
   B: It's at 2:45.

Page 28, Exercise C

1. A: What time is your English class?
   B: It's from 9:15 to 1:15.
2. A: What time is your break?
   B: It's from 11:15 to 11:45.
3. A: What time is your math class?
   B: It's from 12:30 to 2:00.
4. A: What time is your break?
   B: It's from 2:00 to 2:20.

Page 31, Exercise D

1. He goes to work at 7:45.
2. She gets dressed at 8:15.
3. He goes to school at 9:00.
4. She eats breakfast at 6:00.
5. He gets home at 5:30.

Page 32, Exercise B

1. He goes to work at 7:00 on Monday.
2. She goes to school at 5:00 on Wednesday.
3. He gets up at 9:30 on Saturday.
4. She goes to sleep at 10:30 on Tuesday.
5. She goes to the library at 9:00 on Sunday.

Page 34, Exercise B

1. 93   2. 80
3. 17   4. 13
5. 20   6. 79
7. 100   8. 44

Page 36, Exercise A and C

Manny gets up at 6:00.
He gets to work at 7:55. He starts work at 8:00. He is on time.
He goes to school after work.
He gets to class at 5:45. Class starts at 6:00. He is early.
Manny meets friends on Saturday. But he is late!

UNIT 4
Page 39, Exercise B

1. A: Who's that?
   B: That's my father.
2. A: Who's that?
   B: That's my wife.
3. A: Who's that?
   B: That's my husband.
4. A: Who's that?
   B: That's my brother.
5. A: Who's that?
   B: That's my mother.
6. A: Who's that?
   B: That's my daughter.
7. A: Who's that?
   B: That's my grandfather.
8. A: Who's that?
   B: That's my sister.
9. A: Who's that?
   B: That's my grandmother.
10. A: Who's that?
    B: That's my son.

Page 44, Exercise B

1. A: What's the date today?
   B: December second.
2. A: What's the date today?
   B: March seventh.
3. A: What's the date today?
   B: July fifth.

4. A: What's the date today?
   B: August eighteenth.
5. A: What's the date today?
   B: October twenty-second.
6. A: What's the date today?
   B: June thirtieth.

Page 48, Exercise A and C

Lucas and Carla are married. Lucas is Carla's husband. Carla is Lucas's wife.
In their native country, men go to work.
In their native country, women do the household chores.
In the United States, Carla and Lucas go to work.
They both do household chores. Lucas washes the dishes.
Lucas goes to the supermarket, too.

UNIT 5

Page 53, Exercise C

1. A: Do you have change for a five?
   B: Yes. I have five ones.
2. A: Do you have change for a fifty?
   B: Yes. I have a twenty and three tens.
3. A: Do you have change for a ten?
   B: Yes. I have a five and five ones.
4. A: Do you have change for a hundred?
   B: Yes. I have a fifty, a twenty, and three tens.

Page 56, Exercise B

1. twenty-two cents
2. seventy-eight cents
3. sixty-four cents
4. sixteen cents
5. forty-three cents
6. ninety-seven cents

Page 57, Exercise C

1. a dollar fifty-nine
2. eighty-six forty-nine
3. seven twenty-eight
4. fifty-nine sixty-three
5. ninety-five forty
6. thirty-two fifteen

Page 57, Exercise D

1. A: Excuse me. How much is soap?
   B: A dollar seventy-five.
2. A: Excuse me. How much are batteries?
   B: Four seventy-eight.
3. A: Excuse me. How much is aspirin?
   B: Six twenty-nine.

4. A: Excuse me. How much are tissues?
   B: A dollar sixty.
5. A: Excuse me. How much is deodorant?
   B: Three fifteen.
6. A: Excuse me. How much is toilet paper?
   B: Two twenty.

Page 60, Exercise A and C

This is Edna. In her native country, she shops at a market.
She talks about the price. She asks for a better price. She is happy.
In the United States, Edna shops in a big store.
Each item has one price.
Edna pays a good price in the United States, too. She buys things on sale.

UNIT 6

Page 62, Exercise B

1. A: Do we need vegetables?
   B: Yes. Get tomatoes and onions.
2. A: Do we need vegetables?
   B: Yes. Get peppers and mushrooms.
3. A: Do we need vegetables?
   B: Yes. Get cucumbers and lettuce.
4. A: Do we need vegetables?
   B: Yes. Get potatoes and peppers.

Page 65, Exercise B

1. A: Do you like vegetables?
   B: I like peas. I don't like onions.
2. A: Do you like vegetables?
   B: I like potatoes. I don't like peppers.
3. A: Do you like vegetables?
   B: I like tomatoes. I don't like mushrooms.
4. A: Do you like vegetables?
   B: I like cucumbers. I don't like carrots.

Page 71, Exercise B

1. A: Are you ready to order?
   B: I'd like a chicken sandwich, French fries, and juice.
2. A: Are you ready to order?
   B: I'd like a cheeseburger, a green salad, and iced tea.
3. A: Are you ready to order?
   B: I'd like pancakes, a baked potato, and coffee.
4. A: Are you ready to order?
   B: I'd like a tuna fish sandwich, a fruit salad, and tea.

Page 72, Exercise A and C

This is Tran. In his native country, most people eat with chopsticks.

Many children eat with their hands.

This is Riko. In her native country, many people drink soup.

In the United States, most people eat with a fork, knife, and spoon.

They eat sandwiches and French fries with their hands.

UNIT 7

Page 76, Exercise B

1. A: Can you tell me about the apartment for rent?
   B: There is a sunny living room and a small kitchen.
   A: It sounds nice
2. A: Can you tell me about the apartment for rent?
   B: There is a large garage and a sunny dining room.
   A: It sounds nice.
3. A: Can you tell me about the apartment for rent?
   B: There is a large closet and a small basement.
   A: It sounds nice.
4. A: Can you tell me about the apartment for rent?
   B: There is a sunny bedroom and a new kitchen.
   A: It sounds nice.
5. A: Can you tell me about the apartment for rent?
   B: There is a large kitchen and a new bathroom.
   A: It sounds nice.

Page 79, Exercise C

1. A: Is there a stove in the apartment?
   B: Yes, there is.
2. A: Are there any lamps in the apartment?
   B: No, there aren't.
3. A: Are there any chairs in the apartment?
   B: Yes, there are.
4. A: Is there a washing machine in the apartment?
   B: No, there isn't.
5. A: Are there any tables in the apartment?
   B: No, there aren't.
6. A: Is there a bed in the apartment?
   B: Yes, there is.

Page 80, Exercise B

1. 13 Martin Street
2. 50 Angelo Drive
3. 167 Green Boulevard
4. 20 South Lane
5. 184 Meadow Road
6. 1245 Erie Avenue

Page 81, Exercise D and E

A: I'm looking for an apartment.
B: Oh! There's an apartment for rent on my street.
A: What's the address?
B: It's 845 Ocean Avenue.
A: How much is the rent?
B: It's $945 a month.

Page 84, Exercise A and C

This is Pilar. She is 21 years old. She is single.

Pilar lives with her sister and her sister's husband.

Pilar has a good job. She works in an office.

Pilar wants to live with her friends. In the United States, many single people live with friends.

Pilar's parents are not happy. In their native country, single people live with their families.

UNIT 8

Page 87, Exercise B

1. I need a new shirt.
2. I need a new skirt.
3. I need a new T-shirt.
4. I need new sneakers.
5. I need new jeans.
6. I need a new dress.

Page 87, Exercise C

1. A: Let's go shopping! I need a new jacket.
   B: OK. I need shoes.
2. A: Let's go shopping! I need new pants.
   B: OK. I need a dress.
3. A: Let's go shopping! I need a new sweater.
   B: OK. I need a shirt.
4. A: Let's go shopping. I need new sneakers.
   B: OK. I need jeans.

Page 88, Exercise A

1. A: Can I help you?
   B: Do you have this shirt in a large?
   A: Yes. Here you go.
   B: Do you have these sneakers in a size 11?
   A: I'm sorry. We don't.
2. A: Can I help you?
   B: Do you have this dress in a medium?
   A: Yes. Here you go.
   B: Do you have these jeans in a size 10?
   A: I'm sorry. We don't.
3. A: Can I help you?
   B: Do you have this T-shirt in an extra large?
   A: Yes. Here you go.
   B: Do you have these shoes in a size 12?
   A: I'm sorry. We don't.

Page 90, Exercise B

1. Monika is wearing a black jacket.
2. Meg is wearing a red skirt.
3. Jin-Su is wearing a blue shirt.
4. Dora is wearing beige pants.
5. Solomon is wearing white shoes.
6. Li is wearing a purple sweater.
7. Miguel is wearing gray socks.
8. Anne is wearing a blue dress.

Page 93, Exercise D

A: I need to return a sweater and some sneakers.
B: What's the problem?
A: The sweater is too long and the sneakers are too big. Here's my receipt.

Page 95, Exercise C

1. A: What store is having a sale?
   B: Clara's Store is having a sale.
2. A: When is the sale?
   B: The sale is on Thursday.
3. A: What time does the store open?
   B: The store opens at 9:00.
4. A: How much are the jackets?
   B: The jackets are $15.50.
5. A: How much are the shoes?
   B: The shoes are $25.00.
6. A: How much are the shirts?
   B: The shirts are $19.99.

Page 96, Exercise A and C

This is Yun. She lives in the United States. She is getting married.
Her wedding is in August. She needs a new dress. She wants a white dress.
In her native country, people wear white clothes at funerals.
Many women wear a red and green dress at their wedding.
Yun's mother and grandmother want her to have a red and green dress.

UNIT 9
Page 103, Exercise D

A: Hello?
B: Hi, Ming. How's everything going?
A: Great.
B: Is Jack studying English?
A: Yes, he is.
B: Is Mary doing her homework?
A: No, she's not. She's watching TV.

Page 107, Exercise B

1. A: Hello?
   B: Hi. This is Marisa Costas. Can I speak to Mr. Clark?
   A: Mr. Clark is taking a break now. Can I take a message?
   B: Please tell him I'm not coming to work today.
   A: OK. What's your phone number?
   B: It's 212-555-6798.
2. A: Hello?
   B: Hi. This is Ann. Can I speak to Kyoko?
   A: Kyoko is not here. Can I take a message?
   B: Please tell her I'm not going to the movies today.
   A: OK. What's your phone number?
   B: It's 512-555-9841.
3. A: Hello?
   B: Hi. This is Sam White. Can I speak to Ms. Popova?
   A: Ms. Popova is out of the office. Can I take a message?
   B: Please tell her I'm not coming to class today.
   A: OK. What's your phone number?
   B: It's 479-555-8310.

Page 108, Exercise A and C

This is Luis. He lives in the United States. He has two children.
His children are busy on weekends. They talk to their friends. They play sports.
Luis and his wife eat alone on weekends. Their children are busy every Saturday and Sunday.
In Luis's native country, families are together on weekends.
They spend time together. They talk.

UNIT 10
Page 115, Exercise B

1. A: Where are you going?
   B: I'm going to English class.
   A: How do you get to school?
   B: I take the bus.
2. A: Where are you going?
   B: I'm going to work.
   A: Oh. How do you get to work?
   B: I take the train.
3. A: Where are you going?
   B: I'm going to the library.
   A: Oh. How do you get to the library?
   B: I take a taxi.

4. A: Where are you going?
   B: I'm going to the supermarket.
   A: Oh. How do you get to the supermarket?
   B: I drive.

Page 120, Exercise A and C

This is Mohammed.
In Mohammed's native country, he takes the bus to get to work.
He takes the subway to get to English class.
He takes a taxi to go shopping.
Mohammed lives in the United States. He has a car.
In the United States, Mohammed drives to work. He drives to English class. He drives to go shopping.

UNIT 11

Page 123, Exercise B

1. A: What's the problem?
   B: My stomach hurts.
2. A: What's the problem?
   B: My arm hurts.
3. A: What's the problem?
   B: My foot hurts.
4. A: What's the problem?
   B: My ear hurts.
5. A: What's the problem?
   B: My knee hurts.
6. A: What's the problem?
   B: My leg hurts.
7. A: What's the problem?
   B: My neck hurts.
8. A: What's the problem?
   B: My hand hurts.

Page 125, Exercise B

1. Take off your jacket.
2. Sit on the table.
3. Lie down.
4. Step on the scale.

Page 128, Exercise B

A: 911. What's your emergency?
B: Someone robbed my house.
A: Where are you?
B: 15 Main Street in Lake City.
A: What's the cross street?
B: Oak Street.

Page 129, Exercise C

1. A: 911. What's your emergency?
   B: There is a building on fire.
   A: Where are you?
   B: 1402 Oak Avenue in Park City.

A: What's the cross street?
B: Third Street.
2. A: 911. What's your emergency?
   B: My friend is having a heart attack.
   A: Where are you?
   B: 8756 Park Avenue in River City.
   A: What's the cross street?
   B: First Street.
3. A: 911. What's your emergency?
   B: Someone robbed my house.
   A: Where are you?
   B: 4739 Third Avenue in Maple City.
   A: What's the cross street?
   B: Main Street.
4. A: 911. What's your emergency?
   B: There was a car accident.
   A: Where are you?
   B: 3289 Fourth Avenue in Green City.
   A: What's the cross street?
   B: Lake Street.

Page 130, Exercise B

A: Hi, Miguel. How are you?
B: I don't feel well. I have a fever and an ear infection.
A: Oh, that's too bad. Are you taking medicine?
B: Yes. I'm taking prescription medicine.
A: That's good. How often do you take it?
B: I have to take 2 tablets twice a day with water.
A: I hope you feel better soon!

Page 132, Exercise A and C

This is Teresa. She is 45 years old.
In Teresa's native country, people go to the doctor when they are sick.
Teresa lives in the United States. He daughter wants her to get a checkup.
Her daughter says people should go to the doctor every year.
Teresa feels healthy. She does not want to get a checkup.

UNIT 12

Page 144, Exercise A and C

This is Monika. She lives in the United States.
Monika has a job interview on Thursday at 9:00.
Monika is ready for the interview. She practiced her interview skills in her English class.
Monika gets to the interview. She is early. She says hello and smiles.
She shakes hands with Mr. Cruz.
Mr. Cruz asks about Monika's job skills. She answers his questions.

Answer Key

Page 2, Exercise A

1. Canada
2. the United States
3. Mexico
4. Haiti
5. El Salvador
6. Peru
7. Syria
8. China
9. South Korea
10. Somalia
11. Cambodia
12. Vietnam

Page 3, Exercise B

1. Maria; El Salvador
2. Rosa; Haiti
3. Teng; China

Page 4, Exercise A

A B C D E F G H I J K L M N O P Q
R S T U V W X Y Z

Page 4, Exercise B

a b c d e f g h i j k l m n o p q r s t
u v w x y z

Page 4, Exercise C

1. H O N G; C H E N
2. A N N A; N O V A K
3. M A R K; S M I T H
4. C A R L A; D I A Z

Page 5, Exercise A

1. 3   2. 1
3. 8   4. 6
5. 5   6. 9
7. 5   8. 0
9. 7   10. 2

Page 5, Exercise B

1. 53691
2. 02469
3. 26750
4. 63980

Page 5, Exercise C

1. 674-555-5831
2. 829-555-1194
3. 427-555-6850
4. 350-555-7448
5. 914-555-8132
6. 201-555-4990

Page 6, Exercise A

1. am   2. are
3. are   4. am
5. are   6. am
7. are   8. am

Page 6, Exercise B

1. You   2. I
3. I   4. You
5. I   6. You
7. You   8. I

Page 6, Exercise C

1. You're Abdi Hassan.
2. I'm from Somalia.
3. I'm a new student.
4. You're the teacher.
5. I'm from the United States.
6. You're a student.
7. You're in the library.
8. I'm your classmate.

Page 7, Exercise A

1. She   2. He
3. She   4. He

Page 7, Exercise B

1. f   2. c
3. a   4. a
5. b   6. d

Page 8, Exercise C

1. a   2. b
3. a   4. a
5. b   6. a
7. b   8. b

Page 8, Exercise D

1. Lin is my classmate.
   She is my classmate.
   She's my classmate.
2. Marco is from Peru.
   He is from Peru.
   He's from Peru.
3. Eva is my friend.
   She is my friend.
   She's my friend.
4. Akra is from Cambodia.
   He is from Cambodia.
   He's from Cambodia.

Page 9, Exercise A

1. is   2. are
3. is   4. are
5. are   6. is
7. is   8. are

Page 10, Exercise B

1. a   2. b
3. a   4. c
5. b   6. c

Page 10, Exercise C

1. They're from Vietnam.
2. We're new students.
3. You're my friends.
4. They're classmates.
5. You're good teachers.
6. We're from Canada.
7. They're friends.
8. You're good students.
9. We're friends.
10. They're from South Korea.
11. We're in the library.
12. You're classmates.

Page 11, Exercise B

Adult Education Center

First Name	Middle Name	Last Name
Marie	Anne	Miller

Phone Number	Place of Birth
(214) 555-5301	Canada

Student ID Number
67920

Page 12, Exercise A

5 Other students say hello and kiss.

1 This is Ivan. He is a student. Some students say hello and hug.

2 He says hello to his classmates and smiles.

4 Some students say hello and bow.

3 Some students say hello and shake hands.

Page 12, Exercise B

This is Ivan. He is a student.
He says hello to his classmates and smiles.
In his school, some students say hello and shake hands.
Some students say hello and hug.
Some students say hello and bow.
Other students say hello and kiss.

Page 13, Exercise A

3 Sam: Can I help you?

2 Customer: Thank you.

1 Sam: Welcome to Buy Best.

4 Customer: No, thank you. I'm fine.

Page 13, Exercise B

Sam: Welcome to Buy Best.
Customer: Thank you.
Sam: Can I help you?
Customer: No, thank you. I'm fine.

UNIT 2

Page 14, Exercise A

1. b	2. e
3. d	4. c
5. h	6. a
7. i	8. f
9. g	

Page 15, Exercise B

1. b	2. b
3. a	4. a
5. b	

Page 15, Exercise C

1. I do
2. I don't
3. I do
4. I don't
5. I do

Page 16, Exercise A

1. Turn on
2. Take out
3. Open
4. Close
5. Put away
6. Turn off

Page 17, Exercise C

1. Yes	2. No
3. Yes	4. No
5. Yes	

Page 17, Exercise D

1. Don't close your book.
2. Don't use a pencil.
3. Don't turn on the light.
4. Don't take out your notebook.
5. Don't open the door.
6. Don't put away your phone.

Page 18, Exercise A

1. cla_s_sro_o_m
2. re_s_tro_o_m
3. c_o_mput_e_r _l_ab
4. _o_ff_i_ce
5. b_o_okstor_e_
6. t_e_s_t_ing roo_m_
7. l_i_br_a_ry
8. caf_e_teri_a_

Page 19, Exercise B

1. a	2. b
3. a	4. a
5. a	6. b

Page 20, Exercise A

1. next to
2. next to
3. across from
4. across from
5. next to
6. next to

Page 21, Exercise B

1. Yes	2. Yes
3. Yes	4. No
5. No	6. Yes

Page 22, Exercise A

1. c	2. d
3. e	4. b
5. f	6. a

Page 23, Exercise B

A: How do you study English?

B: I _go_ to class, and I _ask_ the teacher questions.

A: That's great!

B: How do you study English?

A: I _practice_ with my classmates. At home, I _write_ in my notebook.

Page 23, Exercise C

1. I use / ~~write~~ a dictionary.
2. I ~~go~~ / read signs.
3. I study / ~~go~~ English at school.
4. I ~~practice~~ / talk to people.
5. I write / ~~ask~~ new words.
6. I ask / ~~practice~~ the teacher questions.
7. I go / ~~use~~ to the library.
8. I ~~study~~ / write in my notebook.
9. I practice / ~~use~~ with my classmates.
10. I ~~talk~~ / go to class.

Page 24, Exercise A

2 In her native country, students do not talk in class.

4 In the United States, students talk in groups.

6 The teacher listens to the students.

1 This is Lan.

3 They listen to the teacher.

5 Students ask questions.

Page 24, Exercise B

This is Lan.
In her native country, students do not talk in class.
They listen to the teacher.
In the United States, students talk in groups.
Students ask questions.
The teacher listens to the students.

Page 25, Exercise A

4 Student: My first name is Rosa. My name is Rosa Sanchez.

5 Alma: Great! Write your first and last name on the form here.

1 Alma: What is your last name?

2 Student: My last name is Sanchez.

3 Alma: OK. What is your first name?

Page 25, Exercise B

Alma: What is your last name?
Student: My last name is Sanchez.
Alma: OK. What is your first name?
Student: My first name is Rosa. My name is Rosa Sanchez.
Alma: Great! Write your first and last name on the form here.

UNIT 3

Page 26, Exercise A

1. b	2. b
3. a	4. a
5. b	6. a

Page 26, Exercise B

1. b	2. e
3. c	4. f
5. a	6. d

Page 27, Exercise C

1. 8:10
2. 3:05
3. 7:15
4. 5:20
5. 12:30
6. 9:45

Page 27, Exercise D

1. It's 8:10
2. What time is it
3. It's 7:15
4. It's 5:20
5. It's 12:30
6. What time is it

Page 28, Exercise A

1. A: *What* time is your English class?
   B: It's *from* 1:00 to 5:00.
   A: What *time* is your break?
   B: It's *at* 2:15.
2. A: What *time* is your English class?
   B: It's from 6:00 *to* 9:00.
   A: What time *is* your break?
   B: It's *at* 7:45.

Page 28, Exercise B

1. a	2. b
3. b	4. a

Page 28, Exercise C

1. It's from *9:15* to *1:15*.
2. It's from *11:15* to *11:45*.
3. It's from *12:30* to *4:00*.
4. It's from *2:00* to *2:20*.

Page 29, Exercise D

1. Yes	2. No
3. No	4. No
5. No	6. Yes
7. No	8. Yes

Page 29, Exercise E

1. The library is open at 9:00.
2. My break is from 2:00 to 2:20.
3. The cafeteria is open from 7:00 to 3:00.

4. My computer class starts at 4:30.
5. The office is open at 11:30.
6. My English class is from 10:00 to 12:00.
7. The computer lab is open from 8:00 to 11:00.
8. My break is over at 3:00.

Page 30, Exercise A

1. c	2. e
3. h	4. f
5. a	6. i
7. d	8. b
9. g	

Page 31, Exercise B

1. goes	2. takes
3. gets	4. eats
5. gets up	6. goes

Page 31, Exercise D

1. a	2. b
3. b	4. a
5. b	

Page 32, Exercise A

From left to right:
Sunday
Monday
Tuesday
Wednesday
Thursday
Friday
Saturday

Page 32, Exercise B

1. a	2. b
3. b	4. a
5. b	

Page 32, Exercise C

1. from; to
2. on
3. on
4. from; to
5. on
6. from; to

Page 33, Exercise E

1. Yes	2. No
3. No	4. No
5. Yes	6. No
7. No	8. No

Page 34, Exercise A

1. seventy-one
2. fifty-nine
3. eleven
4. sixty
5. thirty-three
6. fourteen
7. one hundred
8. ninety
9. forty-seven
10. eighty-six

Page 34, Exercise B

1. 93	2. 80
3. 17	4. 13
5. 20	6. 79
7. 100	8. 44

Page 34, Exercise C

1. a	2. c
3. d	4. b

Page 35, Exercise D

1. two
2. fifteen
3. three
4. twenty

Page 36, Exercise A

3 He goes to school after work.
1 Manny gets up at 6:00.
5 Manny meets friends on Saturday. But he is late!
2 He gets to work at 7:55. He starts work at 8:00. He is on time.
4 He gets to class at 5:45. Class starts at 6:00. He is early.

Page 36, Exercise B

Manny gets up at 6:00.
He gets to work at 7:55. He starts work at 8:00. He is on time.
He goes to school after work.
He gets to class at 5:45. Class starts at 6:00. He is early.
Manny meets friends on Saturday. But he is late!

Page 37, Exercise A

5 Wei: OK. Please call next time.
2 Employee: I'm sorry!
1 Wei: It is 9:10. You're late.
4 Employee: The bus was late. I'm sorry.
3 Wei: Work starts at 9:00. Why are you late?

Page 37, Exercise B

Wei: It is 9:10. You're late.
Employee: I'm sorry!
Wei: Work starts at 9:00. Why are you late?
Employee: The bus was late. I'm sorry.
Wei: OK. Please call next time.

UNIT 4

Page 38, Exercise A

1. a	2. a
3. b	4. a
5. b	6. b
7. a	8. a

Page 39, Exercise B

1. father
2. wife
3. husband
4. brother
5. mother
6. daughter
7. grandfather
8. sister
9. grandmother
10. son

Page 40, Exercise B

1. a	2. b
3. b	4. a
5. a	6. b
7. b	8. a

Page 41, Exercise D

Singular	Plural
parent	parents
brother	brothers
sister	sisters
child	children
grandparent	grandparents
son	sons
daughter	daughters

Page 41, Exercise E

1. sisters
2. parents
3. grandparents
4. brothers
5. children

Page 42, Exercise A

1. vacuum
2. make dinner
3. wash the dishes
4. take out the garbage
5. do the laundry
6. clean the house

Page 43, Exercise B

1. A: _Do you vacuum_?
   B: Yes, _I do._
2. A: _Do you make dinner_?
   B: No, _I don't._
3. A: _Do you clean the house_?
   B: Yes, _I do._
4. A: _Do you wash the dishes_?
   B: No, _I don't._
5. A: _Do you take out the garbage_?
   B: Yes, _I do._
6. A: _Do you do the laundry_?
   B: No, _I don't._

Page 44, Exercise A

1. January
2. February
3. March

4. April
5. May
6. June
7. July
8. August
9. September
10. October
11. November
12. December

Page 44, Exercise B

1. b   2. a
3. a   4. b
5. a   6. b

Page 45, Exercise A

Number	Month
1	January
2	February
3	March
4	April
5	May
6	June
7	July
8	August
9	September
10	October
11	November
12	December

Page 45, Exercise B

1. f   2. d
3. a   4. b
5. c   6. h
7. j   8. e
9. h   10. i

Page 46, Exercise C

1. 4/14/98
2. 6/17/85
3. 9/1/07
4. 2/22/74
5. 3/21/10
6. November 29, 2019
7. July 13, 2022
8. February 8, 1995
9. October 19, 1968
10. May 31, 1983

Page 46, Exercise D

1. 6/20/93
2. 9/30/04
3. 12/6/72
4. 5/30/06
5. 10/17/58
6. 1/9/08
7. 2/25/18
8. 11/4/97
9. 4/2/03

Page 47, Exercise B

Name (First): Ji-yoo
Name (Middle): *leave blank*
Name (Last): Lee
Today's date: *answer will vary*
Date of Birth: 6/1/56
Place of Birth: South Korea
Class: ESL 2
Teacher: Mrs. Baca
Class Schedule (Day/s): Tuesday, Thursday
Class Schedule (Time): 2:00 – 5:00
Class Schedule (Room): 12

Page 48, Exercise A

2   In their native country, men go to work.
5   They both do household chores. Lucas washes the dishes.
6   Lucas goes to the supermarket, too.
1   Lucas and Carla are married. Lucas is Carla's husband. Carla is Lucas's wife.
3   In their native country, women do the household chores.
4   In the United States, Carla and Lucas go to work.

Page 48, Exercise B

Lucas and Carla are married.
Lucas is Carla's husband. Carla is Lucas's wife.
In their native country, men go to work.
In their native country, women do the household chores.

In the United States, Carla and Lucas go to work.
They both do household chores.
Lucas washes the dishes.
Lucas goes to the supermarket, too.

Page 49, Exercise A

2   Coworker: Yes, it is. That's my brother and three sisters.
1   Mara: Is that your family?
3   Mara: Who's that?
4   Coworker: That's my grandmother.
6   Coworker: Thank you!
5   Mara: You have a nice family.

Page 49, Exercise B

Mara: Is that your family?
Coworker: Yes, it is. That's my brother and three sisters.
Mara: Who's that?
Coworker: That's my grandmother.
Mara: You have a nice family.
Coworker: Thank you!

UNIT 5

Page 50, Exercise A

1. b   2. d
3. c   4. e
5. a

Page 50, Exercise B

1. a quarter
2. a nickel
3. a half-dollar
4. a dime
5. a half-dollar

Page 51, Exercise C

1. quarter; dimes; nickels
2. dimes; nickel
3. quarters; dimes; nickel
4. nickels; pennies
5. quarters; dimes

Page 52, Exercise A

1. one
2. five
3. ten
4. twenty
5. fifty
6. one hundred

Page 53, Exercise B

1. twenty dollars
2. ten dollars
3. fifty dollars
4. one hundred dollars

Page 53, Exercise C

1. five; ones
2. fifty; tens
3. ten; five
4. hundred; twenty

Page 54, Exercise A

1. toothpaste
2. paper towels
3. shaving cream
4. toilet paper
5. soap
6. batteries
7. razors
8. deodorant
9. tissues
10. shampoo
11. light bulbs
12. aspirin

Page 55, Exercise B

1. is
2. are
3. is
4. is
5. are
6. are
7. is
8. is

Page 55, Exercise C

1. Where is
2. Where are
3. Where are
4. Where is
5. Where is

Page 56, Exercise A

1. a
2. b
3. b
4. a
5. b

Page 56, Exercise B

1. 22 cents
2. 78 cents
3. 64 cents
4. 16 cents
5. 43 cents
6. 97 cents

Page 57, Exercise C

1. $1.59
2. $86.49
3. $7.28
4. $59.63
5. $95.40
6. $32.15

Page 57, Exercise D

1. $1.75
2. $4.78
3. $6.29
4. $1.60
5. $3.15
6. $2.20

Page 58, Exercise B

1. No
2. No
3. Yes
4. No
5. No

Page 58, Exercise C

1. $5.99
2. $2.99
3. $3.79
4. $5.79
5. $6.99
6. $6.25

Page 59, Exercise D

1. insert your card
2. sign your name
3. swipe your card
4. a card
5. enter your PIN
6. remove your card
7. tap OK

Page 60, Exercise A

3 She is happy.
1 This is Edna. In her native country, she shops at a market.
6 Edna pays a good price in the United States, too. She buys things on sale.
5 Each item has one price.
2 She talks about the price. She asks for a better price.
4 In the United States, Edna shops in a big store.

Page 60, Exercise B

This is Edna. In her native country, she shops at a market.
She talks about the price. She asks for a better price.
In the United States, Edna shops in a big store.
Each item has one price.
Edna pays a good price in the United States, too. She buys things on sale.
She is happy.

Page 61, Exercise A

4 Fatima: The total is $4.95.
3 Customer: OK. I need new batteries.
1 Customer: Excuse me. How much are the batteries?
6 Fatima: Yes, I do.
2 Fatima: Let me see. They're $4.79.
5 Customer: Do you have change for a ten?
7 Customer: Great. Here you go.
8 Fatima: Thank you. Here is your change.

Page 61, Exercise B

Customer: Excuse me. How much
are the batteries?
Fatima: Let me see. They're
$4.79.
Customer: OK. I need new
batteries.
Fatima: The total is $4.95.
Customer: Do you have change
for a ten?
Fatima: Yes, I do.
Customer: Great. Here you go.
Fatima: Thank you. Here is
your change.

UNIT 6

Page 62, Exercise A

1. tomatoes
2. onions
3. cucumbers
4. mushrooms
5. peas
6. carrots
7. lettuce
8. peppers
9. potatoes

Page 62, Exercise B

1. a   2. a
3. b   4. a

Page 63, Exercise D

1. b   2. b
3. b   4. a
5. b   6. a

Page 64, Exercise A

1. I like / ~~don't like~~ <u>potatoes</u>.
   I ~~like~~ / don't like <u>peppers</u>.
2. I like / ~~don't like~~ <u>tomatoes</u>.
   I ~~like~~ / don't like <u>onions</u>.
3. I like / ~~don't like~~ <u>peas</u>.
   I ~~like~~ / don't like <u>lettuce</u>.
4. I like / ~~don't like~~ <u>cucumbers</u>.
   I ~~like~~ / don't like <u>carrots</u>.

Page 65, Exercise B

1. peas; onions
2. potatoes; peppers
3. tomatoes; mushrooms
4. cucumbers; carrots

Page 66, Exercise A

1. apples
2. cherries
3. mangoes
4. strawberries
5. pears
6. oranges
7. bananas
8. peaches
9. grapes

Page 67, Exercise B

1. likes
2. likes
3. doesn't like
4. likes
5. doesn't like
6. doesn't like

Page 67, Exercise C

1. likes grapes
2. doesn't like strawberries
3. likes bananas
4. doesn't like apples
5. likes mangoes
6. doesn't like pears

Page 68, Exercise A

1. a can of soup
2. a bag of rice
3. a loaf of bread
4. a gallon of milk
5. a box of cereal
6. a dozen eggs

Page 69, Exercise B

1. gallons; boxes
2. pounds; bags
3. loaves; boxes
4. pounds; cans

Page 69, Exercise C

1. loaf of bread; gallons of milk
2. box of cereal; bags of rice
3. dozen eggs; cans of soup
4. gallon of milk; boxes of cereal

Page 70, Exercise B

1. $1.79
2. $5.97
3. $3.16
4. $4.25
5. $2.58
6. 49¢

Page 70, Exercise C

1 gallon of milk

3 cans of soup

2 boxes of cereal

1 loaf of bread

2 dozen eggs

Page 71, Exercise A

1. d   2. c
3. a   4. b
5. e   6. f

Page 71, Exercise B

1. a   2. b
3. b   4. b

Page 72, Exercise A

2   Many children eat with their
    hands.
3   This is Riko. In her native
    country, many people drink
    soup.
1   This is Tran. In his native
    country, most people eat with
    chopsticks.
4   In the United States, most
    people eat with a fork, knife,
    and spoon.
5   They eat sandwiches and
    French fries with their hands.

Page 72, Exercise B

This is Tran. In his native country, most people eat with chopsticks. Many children eat with their hands.
This is Riko. In her native country, many people drink soup.
In the United States, most people eat with a fork, knife, and spoon. They eat sandwiches and French fries with their hands.

Page 73, Exercise A

3 Carlos: OK, got it! What about vegetables? What do we need?
6 Sara: Oh! We need three gallons of milk!
1 Carlos: Do we need ground beef?
5 Carlos: Anything else?
2 Sara: Yes, we need four pounds of ground beef.
4 Sara: Let's see, we need carrots, potatoes, and lettuce.

Page 73, Exercise B

Carlos: Do we need ground beef?
Sara: Yes, we need four pounds of ground beef.
Carlos: OK, got it! What about vegetables? What do we need?
Sara: Let's see, we need carrots, potatoes, and lettuce.
Carlos: Anything else?
Sara: Oh! We need three gallons of milk!

UNIT 7

Page 74, Exercise A

1. bedroom
2. kitchen
3. living room
4. dining room
5. bathroom
6. laundry room
7. garage
8. closet

Page 75, Exercise B

bedrooms; bathrooms; kitchen; living room

Page 75, Exercise D

1. No   2. Yes
3. Yes   4. No
5. Yes   6. No
7. No   8. No

Page 76, Exercise A

1. c   2. b
3. d   4. a

Page 76, Exercise B

1. sunny; small
2. large; sunny
3. large; small
4. sunny; new
5. large; new

Page 77, Exercise C

1. is   2. are
3. is   4. is
5. are   6. is
7. are   8. is
9. are   10. is

Page 77, Exercise D

1. There is
2. There are
3. There is
4. There is
5. There are
6. There is
7. There are
8. There is
9. There is
10. There are

Page 78, Exercise A

1. d   2. h
3. g   4. i
5. c   6. b
7. a   8. j
9. e   10. f
11. l   12. m
13. n   14. k

Page 79, Exercise B

1. Is there; there is
2. Are there; there aren't
3. Are there; there aren't
4. Is there; there isn't
5. Are there; there are

Page 79, Exercise C

1. a   2. b
3. a   4. b
5. b   6. a

Page 80, Exercise A

1. 14
2. Bank
3. Boulevard
4. River Road
5. 34 Park
6. 527; Drive

Page 80, Exercise B

1. 13   2. 50
3. 167   4. 20
5. 184   6. 1245

Page 81, Exercise C

1. a   2. b
3. a   4. b
5. a   6. b

Page 81, Exercise E

1. Yes   2. No
3. No

Page 82, Exercise A

1. d   2. g
3. e   4. f
5. c   6. a
7. b

Page 82, Exercise B

1. Yes   2. Yes
3. No   4. Yes
5. No

Page 83, Exercise C

1. Yes
2. Yes
3. No
4. Yes
5. No

Page 84, Exercise A

3 Pilar has a good job. She works in an office.

1 This is Pilar. She is 21 years old. She is single.

4 Pilar wants to live with her friends.

6 Pilar's parents are not happy. In their native country, single people live with their families.

2 Pilar lives with her sister and her sister's husband.

5 In the United States, many single people live with friends.

Page 84, Exercise B

This is Pilar. She is 21 years old. She is single.

Pilar lives with her sister and her sister's husband.

Pilar has a good job. She works in an office.

Pilar wants to live with her friends.

In the United States, many single people live with friends.

Pilar's parents are not happy. In their native country, single people live with their families.

Page 85, Exercise A

5 Vera: There are two bedrooms, a kitchen, and a living room.

2 Customer: Good morning. I'm looking for a two-bedroom apartment.

1 Vera: Good morning. Can I help you?

7 Vera: It's $1,150 a month.

4 Customer: What's it like?

8 Customer: What's the address?

6 Customer: It sounds great! How much is the rent?

9 Vera: It's 32 River Street.

3 Vera: OK. I have an apartment for rent on River Street.

Page 85, Exercise B

Vera: Good morning. Can I help you?

Customer: Good morning. I'm looking for a two-bedroom apartment.

Vera: OK. I have an apartment for rent on River Street.

Customer: What's it like?

Vera: There are two bedrooms, a kitchen, and a living room.

Customer: It sounds great! How much is the rent?

Vera: It's $1,150 a month.

Customer: What's the address?

Vera: It's 32 River Street.

UNIT 8

Page 86, Exercise A

1. sneakers
2. pants
3. a shirt
4. shoes
5. a T-shirt
6. a skirt
7. a jacket
8. a dress
9. jeans
10. a sweater
11. socks

Page 87, Exercise B

1. b
2. a
3. c
4. c
5. a
6. a

Page 87, Exercise C

1. jacket; shoes
2. pants; a dress
3. sweater; a shirt
4. sneakers; jeans

Page 88, Exercise A

1. large; 11
2. medium; 10
3. extra large; 12

Page 88, Exercise B

1. this
2. this
3. These
4. This
5. these

Page 89, Exercise C

1. that
2. those
3. That
4. Those
5. that
6. those

Page 89, Exercise D

1. those
2. this
3. these
4. that

Page 90, Exercise A

1. red
2. orange
3. yellow
4. green
5. blue
6. purple
7. pink
8. beige
9. gray
10. brown
11. black
12. white

Page 90, Exercise B

1. a	2. a
3. b	4. a
5. a	6. b
7. b	8. a

Page 91, Exercise D

1. Yes	2. No
3. No	4. Yes
5. No	6. Yes

Page 92, Exercise A

1. small
2. short
3. long
4. big

Page 92, Exercise B

1. The jacket is too small.
2. The sneakers are too big.
3. The dress is too long.
4. The pants are too short.

Page 93, Exercise C

1. sweater; socks; sweater; long OR big; socks; big
2. dress; pants OR jeans; dress; long; pants OR jeans; small

Page 93, Exercise D

1. b	2. b
3. b	4. a

Page 94, Exercise B

1. Yes	2. Yes
3. No	4. No
5. No	6. Yes
7. No	8. Yes

Page 95, Exercise C

1. Clara's
2. Thursday
3. 9:00
4. $15.50
5. $25.00
6. $19.99

Page 96, Exercise A

3 In her native country, people wear white clothes at funerals.

1 This is Yun. She lives in the United States. She is getting married.

4 Many women wear a red and green dress at their wedding.

5 Yun's mother and grandmother want her to have a red and green dress.

2 Her wedding is in August. She needs a new dress. She wants a white dress.

Page 96, Exercise B

This is Yun. She lives in the United States. She is getting married. Her wedding is in August. She needs a new dress. She wants a white dress.
In her native country, people wear white clothes at funerals.
Many women wear a red and green dress at their wedding.
Yun's mother and grandmother want her to have a red and green dress.

Page 97, Exercise A

3 Omar: OK. What's the problem?

6 Customer: Yes. Here you go.

1 Omar: Good afternoon. Can I help you?

7 Omar: Thank you.

5 Omar: Do you have your receipt?

2 Customer: I need to return these pants.

4 Customer: They are too big.

Page 97, Exercise B

Omar: Good afternoon. Can I help you?
Customer: I need to return these pants.
Omar: OK. What's the problem?
Customer: They are too big.
Omar: Do you have your receipt?
Customer: Yes. Here you go.
Omar: Thank you.

UNIT 9

Page 98, Exercise A

1. c	2. f
3. i	4. e
5. g	6. b
7. a	8. d
9. h	

Page 99, Exercise B

1. Yes	2. Yes
3. No	4. Yes
5. No	6. No
7. No	

Page 100, Exercise A

1. playing the guitar
2. going to the library
3. playing the video games
4. going to the movies

Page 101, Exercise B

1. She's going online.
2. You're playing video games.
3. They're watching TV.
4. We're listening to music.
5. He's going to the movies.
6. I'm playing soccer.
7. She's exercising.
8. You're visiting friends.
9. I'm playing the guitar.

Page 101, Exercise C

1. He's playing soccer.
2. We're going to the movies.
3. I'm going online.
4. She's exercising.
5. They're listening to music.
6. You're watching TV.
7. We're playing the guitar.
8. I'm visiting friends.
9. He's playing video games.

Page 102, Exercise A

1. talk on the phone
2. feed the cat
3. pay bills
4. do homework
5. walk the dog
6. wash the car

Page 102, Exercise B

1. he is
2. she isn't
3. she is
4. they are
5. he isn't
6. they are

Page 103, Exercise C

1. Are you washing the car?
2. Is Evan paying bills?
3. Are Cara and Tom studying English?
4. Is Julie visiting friends?
5. Is he playing soccer?
6. Are we doing homework?

Page 103, Exercise E

1. Yes
2. No
3. No
4. Yes
5. Yes

Page 104, Exercise A

1. work on the computer
2. answer the phone
3. fix cars
4. look for something
5. help a customer
6. take orders
7. take a break
8. count money
9. drive a truck

Page 105, Exercise B

1. he's not
2. they're not
3. I'm not
4. she's not
5. he's not

Page 105, Exercise C

1. She's not driving a truck.
2. He's not talking on the phone.
3. They're not counting money.
4. He's not working on the computer.

Page 106, Exercise A

1. Dan Green
2. February 19, 2018
3. 4:04 P.M.
4. Hana Brown
5. 718-555-2342
6. she's sick
7. Sofia Garcia
8. August 13, 2019
9. 9:32 P.M.
10. Alan Smith
11. he missed the bus

Page 107, Exercise B

1. Caller: Marisa Costas
   Phone: 212-555-6798
   Message: (Answer will vary.)
   She's not coming to work today.
2. For: Kyoko
   Caller: Ann
   Phone: 512-555-9841
   Message: (Answer will vary.)
   She's not going to the movies today.
3. For: Ms. Popova
   Caller: Sam White
   Phone: 479-555-8310
   Message: (Answer will vary.)
   He's not coming to class today.

Page 108, Exercise A

3 Luis and his wife eat alone on weekends.

1 This is Luis. He lives in the United States. He has two children.

6 They spend time together. They talk.

2 His children are busy on weekends. They talk to their friends. They play sports.

5 In Luis's native country, families are together on weekends.

4 Their children are busy every Saturday and Sunday.

Page 108, Exercise B

This is Luis. He lives in the United States. He has two children.
His children are busy on weekends. They talk to their friends. They play sports.
Luis and his wife eat alone on weekends.
Their children are busy every Saturday and Sunday.
In Luis's native country, families are together on weekends.
They spend time together. They talk.

Page 109, Exercise A

3 Ken: Oh! Sorry to bother you. Are you working tonight?

1 Ken: Hi, Pam. It's Ken. What are you doing?

4 Pam: No, I'm not. I'm going home at 5:00. I can call you then.

2 Pam: I'm working right now. Can I call you later?

5 Ken: OK, great. Bye!

Page 109, Exercise B

Ken: Hi, Pam. It's Ken. What are you doing?
Pam: I'm working right now. Can I call you later?
Ken: Oh! Sorry to bother you. Are you working tonight?
Pam: No, I'm not. I'm going home at 5:00. I can call you then.
Ken: OK, great. Bye!

UNIT 10

Page 110, Exercise A

1. f	2. e
3. g	4. b
5. a	6. h
7. i	8. d
9. c	

Page 111, Exercise B

1. a parking lot; Grand Avenue; Second Street
2. a restaurant; Main Avenue; Second Street
3. a gas station; Central Avenue; Second Street
4. a supermarket; Central Avenue; Third Street

Page 112, Exercise A

1. post office
2. park
3. Department of Motor Vehicles (DMV)
4. City Hall
5. fire station
6. school
7. police station
8. library
9. court house

Page 113, Exercise B

1. across from
2. across from
3. between
4. across from
5. between
6. across from
7. between
8. across from

Page 114, Exercise A

1. g	2. d
3. e	4. h
5. a	6. c
7. b	8. i
9. f	

Page 115, Exercise B

1. take the bus
2. take the train
3. take a taxi
4. drive

Page 116, Exercise A

1. Turn left.
2. Turn right.
3. Go straight.
4. Go two blocks.

Page 116, Exercise B

1. Go straight; turn right
2. Turn left; go straight
3. Turn right; turn left

Page 117, Exercise C

1. police station
2. library
3. bank
4. gas station

Page 118, Exercise A

1. no parking
2. don't walk
3. stop
4. no U-turn
5. do not enter
6. one-way street
7. speed limit
8. crosswalk
9. no left turn

Page 119, Exercise B

1. No	2. No
3. Yes	4. No
5. Yes	6. No
7. No	8. No

Page 120, Exercise A

2 In Mohammed's native country, he takes the bus to get to work.

5 Mohammed lives in the United States. He has a car.

1 This is Mohammed.

6 In the United States, Mohammed drives to work.

7 He drives to English class. He drives to go shopping.

3 He takes the subway to get to English class.

4 He takes a taxi to go shopping.

Page 120, Exercise B

This is Mohammed.
In Mohammed's native country, he takes the bus to get to work.
He takes the subway to get to English class.
He takes a taxi to go shopping.
Mohammed lives in the United States. He has a car.
In the United States, Mohammed drives to work.
He drives to English class. He drives to go shopping.

Page 121, Exercise A

2 Ali: Go two blocks to the left. It's across from the fire station.

1 Customer: Excuse me. Where is the library?

5 Customer: Go two blocks and turn left. I understand. Thank you!

6 Ali: You're welcome!

4 Ali: No problem. Go two blocks and turn left on Park Street.

3 Customer: I'm sorry. Can you repeat that?

Page 121, Exercise B

Customer: Excuse me. Where is the library?

Ali: Go two blocks to the left. It's across from the fire station.

Customer: I'm sorry. Can you repeat that?

Ali: No problem. Go two blocks and turn left on Park Street.

Customer: Go two blocks and
turn left. I understand.
Thank you!
Ali: You're welcome!

UNIT 11

Page 122, Exercise A

1. head
2. mouth
3. ear
4. eye
5. nose
6. neck
7. chest
8. stomach
9. hand
10. shoulder
11. back
12. arm
13. knee
14. leg
15. foot / feet

Page 123, Exercise B

1. a	2. b
3. a	4. a
5. b	6. b
7. a	8. a

Page 123, Exercise C

1. neck hurts
2. hand hurts
3. stomach hurts
4. shoulder hurts

Page 124, Exercise A

1. Breath
2. sleeves
3. straight
4. Lie
5. jacket
6. mouth
7. out
8. Step
9. table

Page 125, Exercise B

1. b	2. d
3. a	4. c

Page 125, Exercise D

1. Yes	2. No
3. Yes	4. No
5. Yes	

Page 126, Exercise A

1. e	2. a
3. d	4. h
5. i	6. b
7. c	8. f
9. g	

Page 127, Exercise B

1. take aspirin
2. drink a lot of liquids
3. get a lot of rest
4. stay home from work

Page 127, Exercise C

1. You should take aspirin.
2. You should get a lot of rest.
3. You should stay home from school.
4. You should drink a lot of liquids.

Page 128, Exercise A

1. Someone robbed my house.
2. There was a car accident.
3. My friend is having a heart attack.
4. There is a building on fire.

Page 128, Exercise B

1. a	2. a
3. b	4. b

Page 129, Exercise C

1. fire; 1402
2. heart; 8756
3. robbed; 4739
4. car; 3289

Page 130, Exercise A

1. b	2. a
3. a	4. b
5. b	6. a
7. a	8. b
9. a	

Page 130, Exercise B

1. Yes	2. No
3. Yes	4. Yes
5. No	

Page 131, Exercise D

1. pain and fever
2. aspirin
3. two tablets
4. four hours
5. water
6. doctor

Page 132, Exercise A

3 Teresa lives in the United States.

1 This is Teresa. She is 45 years old.

5 Her daughter says people should go to the doctor every year.

2 In Teresa's native country, people go to the doctor when they are sick.

4 Her daughter wants her to get a checkup.

6 Teresa feels healthy. She does not want to get a checkup.

Page 132, Exercise B

This is Teresa. She is 45 years old.
In Teresa's native country, people go to the doctor when they are sick.
Teresa lives in the United States.
Her daughter wants her to get a checkup.
Her daughter says people should go to the doctor every year.
Teresa feels healthy. She does not want to get a checkup.

Page 133, Exercise A

5 Lila: Of course! Can you come in at 3:00?
2 Patient: Hello. I'd like to make an appointment.
9 Lila: See you then!
4 Patient: My neck hurts. I want to see a doctor.
7 Lila: Ok. How about 4:00?
1 Lila: Thank you for calling Sunshine Clinic. How can I help you?
8 Patient: Perfect. Thank you.
6 Patient: No, I can't. I can come in after 3:30.
3 Lila: Ok. What's the problem?

Page 133, Exercise B

Lila: Thank you for calling Sunshine Clinic. How can I help you?
Patient: Hello. I'd like to make an appointment.
Lila: Ok. What's the problem?
Patient: My neck hurts. I want to see a doctor.
Lila: Of course! Can you come in at 3:00?
Patient: No, I can't. I can come in after 3:30.
Lila: Ok. How about 4:00?
Patient: Perfect. Thank you.
Lila: See you then!

UNIT 12

Page 134, Exercise A

1. f   2. d
3. i   4. b
5. g   6. h
7. a   8. e
9. c

Page 135, Exercise B

1. a mechanic
2. a nursing assistant
3. a construction worker
4. a dentist
5. a bus driver
6. a painter
7. a housekeeper
8. a sales assistant

Page 136, Exercise A

1. a custodian
2. a security guard
3. a cashier
4. an office assistant
5. a factory worker
6. a doctor
7. a cook
8. a server
9. a nurse

Page 137, Exercise B

1. does   2. do
3. does   4. does
5. do   6. do
7. does   8. do

Page 137, Exercise C

1. Where do you work?
2. Where does Nancy work?
3. Where do they work?
4. Where does Rafal work?
5. Where do Tien and Monika work?
6. Where does she work?

Page 138, Exercise A

1. fix something
2. use a computer
3. speak two languages
4. build houses
5. help customers
6. operate machinery
7. use a cash register
8. take care of patients
9. use office machines

Page 139, Exercise B

1. help customers
2. build houses
3. fix cars
4. take care of patients
5. use a cash register
6. use office machines

Page 140, Exercise A

1. I can
2. he can't
3. she can't
4. they can
5. he can

Page 140, Exercise B

Answer for completing the questions:
1. use a computer
2. help customers
3. take care of patients
4. build houses

Page 141, Exercise C

1. A: Can Mrs. Smith speak two languages?
   B: Yes, she can.
2. A: Can Mr. Lim use a computer?
   B: No, he can't.
3. A: Can Ms. Popova fix cars?
   B: Yes, she can.
4. A: Can you build houses?
   B: No, I can't.
5. A: Can Eric and Katrina use a cash register?
   B: Yes, they can.
6. A: Can you help customers?
   B: No, I can't.
7. A: Can Mr. Nowak use office machines?
   B: Yes, he can.
8. A: Can Alex and Marie drive a truck?
   B: No, they can't.

Page 142, Exercise B

1. Yes	2. No
3. Yes	4. Yes
5. No	

Page 143, Exercise D

1. A	2. B
3. A	4. A
5. A	6. B
7. B	8. A

Page 143, Exercise E

1. d	2. e
3. f	4. b
5. a	6. c

Page 144, Exercise A

3 Monika is ready for the interview.

4 She practiced her interview skills in her English class.

1 This is Monika. She lives in the United States.

2 Monika has a job interview on Thursday at 9:00.

5 Monika gets to the interview. She is early.

6 She says hello and smiles.

8 Mr. Cruz asks about Monika's job skills. She answers his questions.

7 She shakes hands with Mr. Cruz.

Page 144, Exercise B

This is Monika. She lives in the United States.
Monika has a job interview on Thursday at 9:00.
Monika is ready for the interview. She practiced her interview skills in her English class.
Monika gets to the interview. She is early.
She says hello and smiles.
She shakes hands with Mr. Cruz.
Mr. Cruz asks about Monika's job skills. She answers his questions.

Page 145, Exercise A

7 Van: Thank you! I can do it now.

6 Manager: OK. Please fill out an application.

5 Van: I can start next week!

2 Manager: OK. Do you have experience?

3 Van: Yes, I do. I work at Tom's Cars now. I have five years of experience.

4 Manager: That's great! When can you begin work?

1 Van: Hello. I'd like to apply for the job.

Page 145, Exercise C

Van: Hello. I'd like to apply for the job.

Manager: OK. Do you have experience?

Van: Yes, I do. I work at Tom's Cars now. I have five years of experience.

Manager: That's great! When can you begin work?

Van: I can start next week!

Manager: OK. Please fill out an application.

Van: Thank you! I can do it now.

Credits

Illustration credits: Luis Briseno, pp. 80, 92; Laurie Conley, pp. 124; Deborah Crowle, pp. 2; ElectraGraphics, pp. 13, 25, 37, 49, 61, 74, 85, 90, 97, 109, 111, 113, 116, 118, 120, 121, 128, 133, 145; Peter Grau, pp. 12, 24, 36, 48, 60, 72, 84, 96, 108, 132, 144; Stephen Hutchings, pp. 89, 125; Brian Hughes, pp. 130; Paul McCusker, pp. 123; Roberto Sadi, pp. 20, 75; Meryl Treatner, PP. 126; Anna Veltfort, pp. 16, 93;

Photo Credits: Front cover: Westend61/Getty Images; Bjoern Lauen/ArabianEye/Getty Images; Hero Images/Getty Images; Manuel Breva Colmeiro/Moment/Getty Images. Page 3 (1): Adamkaz/E+/Getty Images; 3 (2): Victor4/123RF; 3 (3): Jetta Productions Inc/DigitalVision/Getty Images; 4 (1): MoMo Productions/DigitalVision/Getty Images; 4 (2): MStudioImages/E+/Getty Images; 4 (3): Hero Images/Getty Images; 4 (4): FG Trade/E+/Getty Images; 5: Flashpop/DigitalVision/Getty Images; 7 (1) : Adamkaz/E+/Getty Images; 7 (2): Funky-data/E+/Getty Images; 7 (3): Tim Robberts/DigitalVision/Getty Images; 7 (4): 10'000 Hours/DigitalVision/Getty Images; 8 (1): Filadendron/E+/Getty Images; 8 (2): Adamkaz/E+/Getty Images; 8 (3): Guvendemir/E+/Getty Images; 8 (4): FilippoBacci/E+/Getty Images; 9 (1): Caiaimage/Paul Bradbury/Getty Images; 9 (2): Asiseeit/E+/Getty Images; 9 (3): Warrengoldswain/123RF; 9 (4): Alvarez/E+/Getty Images; 9 (5): SolStock/E+/Getty Images; 9 (6): Mark Bowden/123RF; 9 (7): Shapecharge/E+/Getty Images; 9 (8): PeopleImages/E+/Getty Images; 14 (a): Joe Belanger/Shutterstock; 14 (b): Korovin/123RF; 14 (c): Rabia Elif Aksoy/123RF; 14 (d): Olegdudko/123RF; 14 (e): Valkr/Shutterstock; 14 (f): Weerachai Ruttanasopa/Shutterstock; 14 (g): J. Helgason/Shutterstock; 14 (h): Binik/Shutterstock; 14 (i): Bondarchuk/Shutterstock; 15 (1a): Valkr/Shutterstock; 15 (1b): Korovin/123RF; 15 (2a): Binik/Shutterstock; 15 (2b): J. Helgason/Shutterstock; 15 (3a): Bondarchuk/Shutterstock; 15 (3b): Olegdudko/123RF 15 (4a): Weerachai Ruttanasopa/Shutterstock; 15 (4b): Joe Belanger/Shutterstock; 15 (5a): J. Helgason/Shutterstock; 15 (5b): Rabia Elif Aksoy/123RF; 15 (bottom, right): VP Photo Studio/Shutterstock; 18 (1): Hotsum/Shutterstock; 18 (2): Sakaekrung/Shutterstock; 18 (3): Picsfive/123RF; 18 (4): Trekandshoot/Shutterstock; 18 (5): Mint Images/Getty Images; 18 (6): Jack Hollingsworth/Photodisc/Getty Images; 18 (7): Wavebreakmedia/Shutterstock; 18 (8): Dumrongsak/123RF; 19 (1a): Wavebreakmedia/Shutterstock; 19 (1b): Sakaekrung/Shutterstock; 19 (2a): Trekandshoot/Shutterstock; 19 (2b): Dumrongsak/123RF; 19 (3a): Hotsum/Shutterstock; 19 (3b): Picsfive/123RF; 19 (4a): Mint Images/Shutterstock; 19 (4b): Jack Hollingsworth/Getty Images; 19 (5a): Picsfive/123RF; 19 (5b): Wavebreakmedia/Shutterstock; 19 (6a): sakaekrung/Shutterstock; 19 (6b): Trekandshoot/Shutterstock; 22 (a): Wavebreakmediamicro/123RF; 22 (b): Maskot/Getty Images; 22 (c): Rabia Elif Aksoy/123RF; 22 (d): Frederic Cirou/PhotoAlto/Alamy Stock Photo; 22 (e): Wavebreakmedia/Shutterstock; 22 (f): Clynt Garnham Education/Alamy Stock Photo; 28: Kali9/E+/Getty Images; 30 (a): Wong Yu Liang/123RF; 30 (b): Dolgachov/123RF; 30 (c): Andriy Popov/123RF; 30 (d): Stieberszabolcs/123RF; 30 (e): Lightwavemedia/Shutterstock; 30 (f): Di Studio/Shutterstock; 30 (g): Shutterstock; 30 (h): Zohaib Hussain/Getty Images; 30 (i): Fluky Fluky/Shutterstock; 35: Tele52/Shutterstock; 38 (1): Tom Werner/DigitalVision/Getty Images; 38 (2): MoMo Productions/DigitalVision/Getty Images; 38 (3): Richard Drury/DigitalVision/Getty Images; 38 (4): Indeed/Getty Images; 38 (5): Hero Images/Getty Images; 38 (6): Peopleimages/E+/Getty Images; 38 (7): Adriana Varela Photography/Moment/Getty Images; 38 (8): MoMo Productions/DigitalVision/Getty Images; 39: Dmytro Zinkevych/123RF; 42 (1): Andriy Popov/123RF; 42 (2): Thanapol Kuptanisakorn/123RF: 42 (3): Dinis Tolipov/123RF: 42 (4): TinnaPong/Shutterstock; 42 (5): Torwai Suebsri/123RF; 42 (6): Andriy Popov/123RF; 47: T.maz/DigitalVision/Getty Images; 50 (half-dollar): Andrei Kuzmik/Shutterstock; 50 (dime): B Brown/Shutterstock; 50 (nickel): B Brown/Shutterstock; 50 (quarter): B Brown/Shutterstock; 50 (penny): B Brown/Shutterstock; 51 (quarter): B Brown/Shutterstock; 51 (dime): B Brown/Shutterstock; 51 (nickel): B Brown/Shutterstock; 51 (penny): B Brown/Shutterstock; 52 ($1): Onehundred Percent/Alamy Stock Photo; 52 ($5): Jonny White/Alamy Stock Photo; 52 ($10): Onehundred Percent/Alamy Stock Photo; 52 ($20): Art-Studio/Alamy Stock Photo; 52 ($50): Onehundred Percent/Alamy Stock Photo; 52 ($100): Pius Koller/Imagebroker/Alamy Stock Photo; 53 ($10): Onehundred Percent/Alamy Stock Photo; 53 ($5): Jonny White/Alamy Stock Photo; 53 ($1): Onehundred Percent/Alamy Stock Photo; 53 ($20): Art-Studio/Alamy Stock Photo; 53 ($50): Onehundred Percent/Alamy Stock Photo; 54 (1): Leah-Anne Thompson/Shutterstock; 54 (2): Alexandr Vlassyuk/Shutterstock; 54 (3): Jvart/123RF; 54 (4): Jane Waterbury/123RF; 54 (5): Jiri Hera/Shutterstock; 54 (6): Sergey Soldatov/123RF; 54 (7): Murat Baysan/123RF; 54 (8): Sergey Kolesnikov/123RF; 54 (9): Pixelrobot/123RF; 54 (10): Mihalec/Shutterstock; 54 (11): Somchai Somsanitangkul/123RF; 54 (11): Somchai Somsanitangkul/123RF; 54 (12): Hurst Photo/Shutterstock; 55: Hispanolistic/E+/Getty Images; 56 ($5): Jonny White/Alamy Stock Photo; 56 (quarter): B Brown/Shutterstock; 56 (penny): B Brown/Shutterstock; 56 ($10): Onehundred Percent/Alamy Stock Photo 56 ($1): Onehundred Percent/Alamy Stock Photo; 56 (dime): B Brown/Shutterstock; 56 (nickel): B Brown/Shutterstock; 56 ($20): Art-Studio/Alamy Stock Photo; 56 ($100): Pius Koller/Imagebroker/Alamy Stock Photo; 57 (1): Jiri Hera/Shutterstock; 57 (2): Sergey Soldatov/123RF; 57 (3): Hurst Photo/Shutterstock; 57 (4): Pixelrobot/123RF; 57 (5): Sergey Kolesnikov/123RF; 57 (6): Jane Waterbury/123RF; 62 (1): Irochka/123RF; 62 (2): Tadeusz Wejkszo/123RF; 62 (3): Daniel vincek/123RF; 62 (4): Sergey Kolesnikov/123RF; 62 (5): Julija Sapic/123RF; 62 (6): 5 Second Studio/Shutterstock; 62 (7): Jiang Hongyan/Shutterstock; 62 (8): Maria Dryfhout/123RF; 62 (9): Geo Martinez/Shutterstock; 63: Westend61/Getty Images; 64 (potatoes): Geo Martinez/Shutterstock; 64 (peppers): Maria Dryfhout/123RF; 64 (tomatoes): Irochka/123RF; 64 (onions): Tadeusz Wejkszo/123RF; 64 (peas): Julija Sapic/123RF; 64 (lettuce): Jiang Hongyan/Shutterstock; 64 (cucumbers): Daniel vincek/123RF; 64 (carrots): 5 Second Studio/Shutterstock; 66 (1) Aneva/123RF; 66 (2): Oleg Vydyborets/123RF; 66 (3): Pushishdonhongsa/123RF; 66 (4): LianeM/Shutterstock; 66 (5): Bryljaev/123RF; 66 (6): Paulo Leandro Souza de Vilela Pinto/123RF; 66 (7): Provasilich/Shutterstock; 66 (8): Viktar Malyshchyts/123RF; 66 (9): Karramba Production/Shutterstock; 67 (grapes): Karramba Production/Shutterstock; 67 (strawberries): LianeM/Shutterstock; 67 (bananas): Provasilich/Shutterstock; 67 (apples): Aneva/123RF; 67 (mangoes): Pushishdonhongsa/123RF; 67 (pears): Bryljaev/123RF; 68 (1): Martinbech/123RF; 68 (2): Gulyash/Shutterstock; 68 (3): V.S.Anandhakrishna/Shutterstock; 68 (4): Bestv/Shutterstock; 68 (5): George Tsartsianidis/123RF; 68 (6): Stable/Shutterstock; 69 (bread): V.S.Anandhakrishna/Shutterstock; 69 (milk): Bestv/Shutterstock; 69 (cereal): George Tsartsianidis/123RF; 69 (rice): Gulyash/Shutterstock; 69 (eggs): Stable/Shutterstock; 69 (soup): Martinbech/123RF; 70 (bread): V.S. Anandhakrishna/Shutterstock; 70 (eggs): Stable/Shutterstock; 70 (chicken): Jiang Hongyan/Shutterstock; 70 (soup): Martinbech/123RF; 70 (cereal): George Tsartsianidis/123RF; 70 (bananas):Viktar Malyshchyts/Shutterstock; 70 (milk): Bestv/Shutterstock; 71 (cereal): Jenifoto/123RF; 71 (eggs & toast): Belchonock/123RF; 71 (pancakes): Hurst Photo/Shutterstock; 71 (fruit salad): Nataliia Kravchuk/123RF; 71 (juice): VictoriaKh/Shutterstock; 71 (tea): Denis Larkin/Shutterstock; 71 (chicken sandwich): Liv friis-larsen/Shutterstock; 71 (French fries): Noophoto/Shutterstock; 71 (baked potato): Timolina/123RF; 71 (cheeseburger): Foodandmore/123RF; 71 (iced tea): Brent Hofacker/123RF; 71 (green salad): Rafalstachura/123RF; 71 (3a, coffee): Edyta Pawlowska/ Shutterstock; 71 (tuna sandwich): Gilberto Mevi/123RF; 74 (1): Glenn Young/Shutterstock; 74 (2): Trevorhirst/E+/Getty Images; 74 (3): Interior Design/Shutterstock; 74 (4): Iriana Shiyan/Shutterstock; 74 (5): Iriana88w/123RF; 74 (6): Hero Images/Getty Images; 74 (7): Sadik Demiroz/Photodisc/Getty Images; 74 (8): Daniela Duncan/Moment/Getty Images; 75: Cecilie_Arcurs/E+/Getty Images; 76 (a): Breadmaker/123RF; 76 (b): David Ronald Head/123RF; 76 (c): Alexandre Zveiger/123RF; 76 (d): Katarzyna Białasiewicz/123RF; 78 (a): Rosley Majid/EyeEm/Getty Images; 78 (b): Wa Nity Canthra/EyeEm/Getty Images; 78 (c): PeopleImages/E+/Getty Images; 78 (d): Lena Koller/Getty Images; 78 (e): Hero Images/Getty Images; 78 (f): Westend61/Getty Images; 78 (g): Jonathan Kitchen/DigitalVision/Getty Images; 78 (h): Westend61/Getty Images; 78 (i): Gerenme/E+/Getty Images; 78 (j): Kentaroo Tryman/Maskot/Getty Images; 78 (k): Martin Barraud/OJO Images/Getty Images; 78 (l): Siraphol Siricharattakul/EyeEm/Getty Images; 78 (m): Gen Sadakane/EyeEm/Getty Images; 78 (n): Pakorn Kumruen/EyeEm/Getty Images; 79: Kate_sept2004/E+/Getty Images; 86 (1): DR-images/Shutterstock; 86 (2): Olga Popova/Shutterstock; 86 (3): Nadezda Tsepaeva/123RF; 86 (4): Elnur/Shutterstock; 86 (5): Vetasster/Shutterstock; 86 (6): Karkas/Shutterstock; 86 (7): Anatoliy Sadovskiy/123RF; 86 (8): Tarzhanova/123RF; 86 (9): Karkas/Shutterstock; 86 (10): Ruslan Kudrin/Shutterstock; 86 (11): Evikka/Shutterstock; 87 (jacket): Anatoliy Sadovskiy/123RF; 87 (shirt): Nadezda Tsepaeva/123RF; 87 (t-shirt): Vetasster/Shutterstock; 87 (skirt): Karkas/Shutterstock; 87 (jeans): Karkas/Shutterstock; 87 (maxi dress): Tarzhanova/123RF; 87 (sweater): Ruslan Kudrin/Shutterstock; 87 (socks): Evikka/Shutterstock; 87 (shoes): Elnur/Shutterstock; 87 (sneakers): DR-images/Shutterstock; 87 (pant): Olga Popova/Shutterstock; 88: Hispanolistic/E+/Getty Images; 91: Jack Hollingsworth/DigitalVision/Getty Images; 94 (shirt): Karkas/Shutterstock; 94 (shoes): Heinteh/123RF; 94 (skirt): Karkas/Shutterstock; 94 (jeans): Elnur/Shutterstock; 94 (sweater): Karkas/Shutterstock; 94 (jacket): Elenovsky/Shutterstock; 95: Blend Images - Erik Isakson/Getty Images; 98 (a): Hongqi Zhang/123RF; 98 (b): Takayuki/Shutterstock; 98 (c): Robert Kneschke/ Shutterstock; 98 (d): Prod-akszyn/Shutterstock; 98 (e): Ferli/123RF; 98 (f): Shutterstock; 98 (g): Syda Productions/Shutterstock; 98 (h): Stockbroker/123RF; 98 (i): Coleman Yuen/Pearson Education Asia Ltd; 100 (woman on phone): 10'000 Hours/DigitalVision/Getty Images; 100 (man on phone): Gstockstudio/123RF; 102 (1): Shutterstock; 102 (2): Littlekidmoment/Shutterstock; 102 (3): Rocketclips, Inc./Shutterstock; 102 (4): Adrin Shamsudin/Shutterstock; 102 (5): Moodboard stock photography/123RF; 102 (6): Volkovslava/Shutterstock; 104 (1): Burlingham/Shutterstock; 104 (2): Shutterstock; 104 (3): AntonioDiaz/Shutterstock; 104 (4): Wavebreak Media Ltd/123RF; 104 (5): Kadmy/123RF; 104 (6): Auremar/123RF; 104 (7): Belchonock/123RF; 104 (8): Maryna Pleshkun/123RF; 104 (9): Robert Carner/123RF; 105 (truck driver): Mint Images/Getty Images; 105 (man on phone): PeopleImages/E+/Getty Images; 105 (bank teller): Hiya Images/Corbis/Getty Images; 105 (man with laptop): Eva-Katalin/E+/Getty Images; 110 (a): Daniil Peshkov/123RF; 110 (b): V. J. Matthew/Shutterstock; 110 (c): Mixa/Sourcenext/Alamy Stock Photo; 110 (d): Wizdata/Shutterstock; 110 (e): Ledomstock/Shutterstock; 110 (f): 06photo/Shutterstock; 110 (g): Shutterstock; 110 (h): Hiya Images/Corbis/Getty Images; 110 (i): Sandsun/Shutterstock; 112 (1): Ken Wolter/Shutterstock; 112 (2): Bildagentur Zoonar GmbH/Shutterstock; 112 (3): Ellen Clark/Alamy Stock Photo; 112 (4): Steve Heap/Shutterstock; 112 (5): Glen Jones/Shutterstock; 112 (6): Stockbroker/123RF; 112 (7): David R. Frazier/DanitaDelimont.com"Danita Delimont Photography"/Newscom; 112 (8): Lim Yong Hian/Shutterstock; 112 (9): Patrick baehl de Lescure/Shuttersock; 114 (a): Martin Novak/Shutterstock; 114 (b): Tetra Images/Getty Images; 114 (c): Maskot/Getty Images; 114 (d): Kristi Blokhin/Shutterstock; 114 (e): Dean Drobot/123RF; 114 (f): Patti McConville/Alamy Stock Photo; 114 (g): BraunS/E+/Getty Images; 114 (h): Leezsnow/iStock/Getty Images; 114 (i): Luciano Leon/Alamy Stock Photo; 118 (1): Georgios Kollidas/Shutterstock; 118 (2): Steve Hamblin/Alamy Stock Photo; 118 (3): Sue Smith/Shutterstock; 118 (4): Robert J. Beyers II/Shutterstock; 118 (5): Creative icon styles/Shutterstock; 118 (6): Sue Smith/Shutterstock; 118 (7): Hank Shiffman/Shutterstock; 118 (9): Robert J. Beyers II/Shutterstock; 119 (walk sign): Steve Hamblin/Alamy Stock Photo; 119 (don't walk sign): Steve Hamblin/Alamy Stock Photo; 119 (stop sign): Sue Smith/Shutterstock; 119 (no parking sign): Georgios Kollidas/Shutterstock; 119 (one way sign): Sue Smith/Shutterstock; 119 (no left turn sign): Robert J. Beyers II/Shutterstock; 119 (do not enter sign): Creative icon styles/Shutterstock; 119 (no u-turn sign): Robert J. Beyers II/Shutterstock; 122 (man, front): Ebtikar/Shutterstock; 122 (man, back): Ebtikar/Shutterstock; 125: Mark Bowden/123RF; 127 (aspirin): James Steidl/Shutterstock; 127 (coffee, juice & water): Nattanit Pumpuang/123RF; 127 (sick woman): Subbotina Anna/Shutterstock; 127 (woman on phone): Shutterstock; 134 (a): Michaeljung/Shutterstock; 134 (b): Michaeljung/Shutterstock; 134 (c): Steve Debenport/E+/Getty Images; 134 (d): Dglimages/123RF; 134 (e): Hongqi Zhang/123RF; 134 (f): Shutterstock; 134 (g): Dolgachov/123RF; 134 (h): Michaeljung/Shutterstock; 134 (i): Dean Drobot/Shutterstock; 135 (1): JohnnyGreig/E+/Getty Images; 135 (2): Shapecharge/E+/Getty Images; 135 (3): Hero Images/Getty Images; 135 (4): Skynesher/E+/Getty Images; 135 (5): Kali9/E+/Getty Images; 135 (6): DNY59/E+/Getty Images; 135 (7): RuslanDashinsky/E+/Getty Images; 135 (8): Tdub303/E+/Getty Images; 136 (1): Andrey_Popov/Shutterstock; 136 (2): PaylessImages/123RF; 136 (3): Odua Images/Shutterstock; 136 (4): Steven Vona/Shutterstock; 136 (5): Kadmy/123RF; 136 (6): PT Images/Shutterstock; 136 (7): Hill Street Studios/DigitalVision/Getty Images; 136 (8): Nakamasa/Shutterstock; 136 (9): Rob Marmion/Shutterstock; 138 (1): Andriy Popov/123RF; 138 (2): Lucky Business/Shutterstock; 138 (3): Koh Sze Kiat/Shutterstock; 138 (4): Sue Smith/Shutterstock; 138 (5): Ferli/123RF; 138 (6): Dmitry Kalinovsky/Shutterstock; 138 (7): Jens Brüggemann/123RF; 138 (8): Mark Bowden/123RF; 138 (9): Chutima Chaochaiya/Shutterstock; 139: Steve Debenport/E+/Getty Images; 140 (woman at computer): Lucky Business/Shutterstock; 140 (help customers): Ferli/123RF; 140 (healthcare worker): Mark Bowden/123RF: 140 (builder): Sue Smith/Shutterstock; 141: 10'000/ Hours/DigitalVision/Getty Images.